AN INTRODUCTION
TO
ALGEBRAIC TOPOLOGY

CONTEMPORARY UNDERGRADUATE MATHEMATICS SERIES
Robert J. Wisner, Editor

MATHEMATICS FOR THE LIBERAL ARTS STUDENT
Fred Richman, Carol Walker, and Robert J. Wisner

INTERMEDIATE ALGEBRA
Edward D. Gaughan

MODERN MATHEMATICS: AN ELEMENTARY APPROACH,
SECOND EDITION
Ruric E. Wheeler

FUNDAMENTAL COLLEGE MATHEMATICS: NUMBER SYSTEMS
AND INTUITIVE GEOMETRY
Ruric E. Wheeler

MODERN MATHEMATICS FOR BUSINESS STUDENTS
Ruric E. Wheeler and W. D. Peeples

ANALYTIC GEOMETRY
James E. Hall

INTRODUCTORY GEOMETRY: AN INFORMAL APPROACH
James R. Smart

AN INTUITIVE APPROACH TO ELEMENTARY GEOMETRY
Beauregard Stubblefield

TOPICS IN GEOMETRY FOR TEACHERS
Paul B. Johnson and Carol H. Kipps

LINEAR ALGEBRA
James E. Scroggs

AN INTRODUCTION TO ABSTRACT ALGEBRA
A. Richard Mitchell and Roger W. Mitchell

INTRODUCTION TO ANALYSIS
Edward D. Gaughan

A PRIMER OF COMPLEX VARIABLES
WITH AN INTRODUCTION TO ADVANCED TECHNIQUES
Hugh J. Hamilton

CALCULUS OF SEVERAL VARIABLES
E. K. McLachlan

PROBABILITY
Donald R. Barr and Peter W. Zehna

✝THEORY AND EXAMPLES OF POINT-SET TOPOLOGY
John Greever

AN INTRODUCTION TO ALGEBRAIC TOPOLOGY
John W. Keesee

AN INTRODUCTION TO ALGEBRAIC TOPOLOGY

John W. Keesee
University of Arkansas

BROOKS/COLE PUBLISHING COMPANY
Belmont, California
A Division of Wadsworth Publishing Company, Inc.

L. C. Cat. Card No.: 78-89507
Printed in the United States of America

PREFACE

This book is designed for use in a one-semester introductory course in algebraic topology at the senior and first-year-graduate levels. Prerequisites are semester courses in general topology, linear algebra, and abstract algebra. The plan of the book is to work out just enough simplicial homology theory so that significant geometric applications may be presented. Perhaps some of the more satisfying applications of this theory are proofs of theorems whose statements do not involve the ideas or vocabulary of homology. For example, the Brouwer Fixed-Point Theorem, the Borsuk-Ulam Theorem, and the separation theorems of Borsuk can be understood by the student with a knowledge of general topology only. Also there are propositions such as the Lefschetz Fixed-Point Theorem and

Hopf's theorem on the degree of a map whose statements involve at least indirectly the ideas of homology. Proofs of these results should convince the reader of the power and utility of homology theory.

In Chapters I and II there is a development of the minimum of simplicial homology theory sufficient to provide a basis for proofs of the theorems mentioned above. The theorems themselves are proved in Chapter III.

This program does not allow for the inclusion of a variety of topics frequently covered in introductory algebraic topology books. For example, there is no mention of excision or exactness, and the subjects of cohomology and singular homology go untouched. The temptation to include the classification of compact surfaces has been resisted. In general, a topic is included only if it contributes to reaching the applications in Chapter III in the shortest possible time.

The Introduction is independent of the rest of the book, its intended purpose being to motivate the reader and to sustain him through the work of Chapters I and II.

It is useless to elaborate on the debt the author owes to many writers in the field of algebraic topology. Special acknowledgment, however, is due to Professors Manuel Berri of Louisiana State University, Charles Greathouse of Samford University, Newcomb Greenleaf of the University of Rochester, Warren M. Krueger of New Mexico State University, Robert H. McDowell of Washington University, St. Louis, and Melvin Thornton of the University of Wisconsin for their helpful comments and suggestions in the manuscript stage.

John W. Keesee

CONTENTS

INTRODUCTION

The most elementary applications of the methods of algebraic topology are in the proofs of various theorems involving mappings of certain subspaces of Euclidean spaces. In this book the necessary preliminary machinery for some of these proofs is built up in Chapters I and II and a number of mapping theorems are proved in Chapter III. The material of the first two chapters is an exposition of some of the beginning aspects of the so-called simplicial homology theory. The applications of this theory and its variants go far beyond those presented here. Otherwise, the theorems of Chapter III would be a rather meager pay-off for the amount of work done in preparation.

An inherent difficulty to be overcome in developing an apprecia-
tion of the power of homology theory lies in the fact that even the simplest
applications must be postponed until the theory itself has been worked out
—a time consuming task. It is possible, however, to prove restricted versions
of some of the theorems mentioned above by methods which, despite their
essentially geometric nature, do in many cases contain germs of the ideas
used later. In this Introduction, examples of some of these restricted
theorems will be given. Their purpose is to provide a glimpse of things to
come, and hopefully to make it plausible to the reader that the proofs in
Chapter III will provide at least a measure of compensation for the tedium
of the first two chapters.

Since no use will be made of this introductory material in sub-
sequent chapters, a considerable lack of rigor will be permitted. The proofs
will be intuitive in the sense that no detailed justification will be attempted
for any fact which seems geometrically obvious. These introductory
theorems are low dimensional cases of general results whose proofs in
Chapter III will be more respectable according to current standards.

The definitions of several subspaces of Euclidean spaces will now
be given.

DEFINITION 1. *Euclidean 2-space* (or the Euclidean plane) is
the set R^2 of all ordered pairs (x, y) of real numbers.

The *disk* E^2 is the subset of R^2 consisting of all ordered pairs (x, y)
such that $x^2 + y^2 \leq 1$.

The *circle* S^1 is the subset of R^2 consisting of all ordered pairs
(x, y) such that $x^2 + y^2 = 1$.

Euclidean 3-space is the set R^3 of all ordered triples (x, y, z) of real
numbers.

The *sphere* S^2 is the subset of R^3 consisting of all ordered triples
(x, y, z) such that $x^2 + y^2 + z^2 = 1$.

All of the sets of Definition 1 are topologized by giving them the
ordinary topology of Euclidean spaces. The plane R^2 can be identified with
the subset of R^3 given by the equation $z = 0$. The circle S^1 is contained in
the disk E^2 and is its point-set boundary in R^2. An element of R^2 or R^3
is called a *point*.

Vector notation will be used for points in R^2 and R^3. For example, if $P = (x, y, z)$ and $Q = (x', y', z')$ are points then $P + Q = (x + x', y + y', z + z')$, $-P = (-x, -y, -z)$, and the *length* of P is the number $\|P\| = (x^2 + y^2 + z^2)^{1/2}$. If P is a point of S^1 or S^2, then its *antipodal point* $-P$ is also a point of S^1 or S^2.

One more definition will be needed.

DEFINITION 2. A topological space X is said to have the *fixed-point property* provided each continuous function $f : X \to X$ has a fixed point; that is, there exists a point $x \in X$ such that $f(x) = x$.

We are now in a position to state two theorems.

THEOREM 1. The disk E^2 has the fixed-point property.

THEOREM 2. Any continuous function $f : S^2 \to R^2$ maps some pair of antipodal points into a common image point; that is, there exists a point $P \in S^2$ such that $f(P) = f(-P)$.

The proofs of these theorems depend strongly on the concept of a *vector distribution* on a set X. We shall restrict attention to the case where X is a subset of R^2.

DEFINITION 3. A vector distribution on a subspace X of R^2 is a continuous function V which assigns to each element (x, y) of X a two-dimensional vector $V(x, y)$.

According to this definition a vector distribution on X is simply a continuous function from X to R^2. However, it will be convenient to picture the distribution V as follows. Suppose that for each (x, y) in X, $V(x, y)$ is a little arrow in the plane R^2 lying with its tail at the point (x, y) and pointing away from (x, y) in a definite direction and having a definite length. It is, of course, possible that for some (x, y) the length of $V(x, y)$ is zero, but we shall be interested only in nonzero distributions, distributions with the property that for each (x, y) in X, $V(x, y) \neq 0$.

Now consider the case where V is a nonzero distribution defined on a set C which is a circle in the plane R^2. We wish to define the *winding number* of such a distribution V. For this purpose, suppose that for each point (x, y) in C the vector $V(x, y)$ has been transported so that its tail is now at the origin $(0, 0)$ in R^2 rather than at (x, y), and that its length and direction have been preserved. Next consider a definite point (x, y) on the circle C and the associated vector $V(x, y)$ at the origin. We may now imagine that the point (x, y) moves once around the circle C in a counterclockwise direction and returns to its original position. At the same time, the vector $V(x, y)$ will rotate about the origin and return to its original position. The fact that the rotating vector returns to its original position means that the total angle through which it turns about the origin is an integral multiple of one complete revolution. In other words, the total net angle of revolution is equal to $2n\pi$ for some integer n. One might compute the integer n by decomposing the circle C into a large number of small arcs, the ith arc having endpoints (x_i, y_i) and (x_{i+1}, y_{i+1}). Let V_i stand for the vector $V(x_i, y_i)$ and A_i for the angle between the vectors V_i and V_{i+1}. The number $2n\pi$ is now the algebraic sum of the angles A_i. It should be fairly clear how this definition could be made precise by a limiting process. The integer n appearing in the expression $2n\pi$ may be positive, negative, or zero and is defined as the winding number of the distribution V. The figure on page 5 illustrates a distribution for which the winding number equals $+1$.

Two preliminary results must be established before the proof of Theorem 1 is given. First we must consider the possibility of extending a nonzero distribution on S^1 to a nonzero distribution on E^2. The question is, given a nonzero vector distribution V on S^1, does there exist a nonzero vector distribution W on E^2 such that W restricted to S^1 is the distribution V? If such a distribution W exists, then V can be extended to E^2. Note that the extension W is always required to be a nonzero distribution. A necessary condition for V to be extendable to E^2 will be given in Lemma 2.

> LEMMA 1. Let V_1 and V_2 be nonzero distributions on a circle C such that for no point (x, y) on C do the vectors $V_1(x, y)$ and $V_2(x, y)$ have the same directions. Then the winding numbers of V_1 and V_2 are the same.

Proof: It is clear that if the winding number of V_1 is greater than that of V_2, then as the point (x, y) traverses the circle C, the rotating vector V_1 must overtake and pass the vector V_2. By the intermediate value theorem it follows that for some point (x, y), $V_1(x, y)$ and $V_2(x, y)$ must have the same direction. This completes the proof.

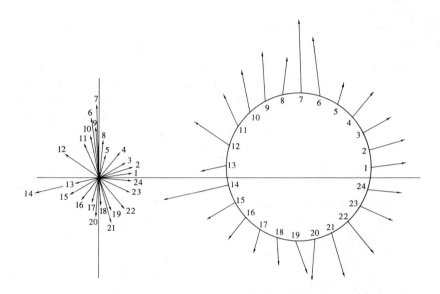

It should be pointed out that in the statement of Lemma 1 it is not actually necessary that the distributions V_1 and V_2 be defined on the same circle. For example, a one-to-one correspondence can be set up between the points of two concentric circles so that the conclusion of the lemma still holds. Observe also that if V is a nonzero distribution on a circle C and $-V$ is the distribution on C given by $-V(x, y) = -(V(x, y))$, then V and $-V$ have the same winding number. As a consequence, an alternative statement of Lemma 1 is that if V_1 and V_2 never have opposite directions, then the winding numbers are the same. A final observation is that a constant nonzero vector distribution on C has winding number zero. These remarks will be used in the proof of the next lemma.

LEMMA 2. If a vector distribution V on S^1 can be extended to E^2, then the winding number of V is zero.

Proof: Suppose that V is a nonzero distribution on S^1 and that W is an extension of V to E^2. Let C_1 be a circle with center at the origin in R^2

and radius less than 1. Then C_1 is contained in E^2 and we may let V_1 be the restriction of W to C_1. Points (x, y) and (x_1, y_1) on S^1 and C_1 respectively will be called corresponding points provided they are on the same ray from the origin. Since W is a uniformly continuous function on the compact set E^2, the radius of C_1 may be taken so large that the angle between vectors assigned to corresponding points on S^1 and C_1 is always less than π. Consequently, vectors assigned by W to corresponding points on S^1 and C_1 never have opposite directions and it can be concluded by Lemma 1 that the winding numbers of V and V_1 are the same. Repetition of this argument shows that we may finally arrive at a circle C_0 with center at the origin and arbitrarily small radius such that the distribution V_0 obtained by restricting W to C_0 has a winding number equal to that of V. Again by the continuity of W, we may take the radius of C_0 so small that the angle between any vector $V_0(x, y)$ and the vector $W(0, 0)$ at the origin is less than π. Now by the final remark preceding the statement of Lemma 2 we see that the winding number of V_0, and also that of V, is zero.

THEOREM 1. The disk E^2 has the fixed-point property.

Proof: Assume that there exists a continuous function $f : E^2 \to E^2$ with no fixed point. This assumption will lead to a contradiction involving a vector distribution defined in terms of the function f. Let us then, for each point (x, y) of E^2, define the vector $W(x, y)$ to be $f(x, y) - (x, y)$. This is the vector with one end at (x, y), the other at $f(x, y)$, and it points from (x, y) to $f(x, y)$. Since $f(x, y) \neq (x, y)$ we see that $W(x, y) \neq 0$, and since the function f is continuous, so also is the distribution W. Next consider two vector distributions on S^1, V and V', where V is obtained by restricting W to S^1, and V' assigns to (x, y) the unit vector from the origin to the point (x, y). Notice that the vector $V(x, y)$ always points into the disk E^2 and that the vector $V'(x, y)$ always points away from the disk. Therefore the two vectors never coincide in direction and the winding numbers of V and V' are equal. It is easy to see that the winding number of V' is $+1$ since as the point (x, y) goes around the circle S^1, the vector $V'(x, y)$ revolves once around the origin. Therefore the winding number of V must also be $+1$. On the other hand, the winding number of V must be zero since W is an extension of V to E^2. This is the contradiction which completes the proof.

EXERCISE

A subset Y of a space X is said to be a *retract* of X provided there exists a map $r : X \to Y$ such that $r \mid Y$ is the identity map of Y. Prove:

(a) If Y is a retract of X and X has the fixed-point property, then so does Y.

(b) S^1 does not have the fixed-point property.

(c) S^1 is not a retract of E^2.

One additional result concerning winding numbers will be used in the proof of Theorem 2.

LEMMA 3. Let V be a nonzero vector distribution on S^1 such that for each $(x, y) \in S^1$, $V(-x, -y) = -V(x, y)$; then the winding number of V is an odd integer.

Proof: Let us first consider the angle of rotation of the vector $V(x, y)$ as the point (x, y) traverses only the upper semicircle of S^1, moving from $(1, 0)$ to $(-1, 0)$. Since $V(-1, 0) = -V(1, 0)$ the net angle of revolution during this time is an odd multiple of π, say $(2n + 1)\pi$. Next, because the distribution satisfies $-V(x, y) = V(-x, -y)$ it is clear that as the point (x, y) traverses the lower half of S^1, the rotation of $V(x, y)$ is exactly the same as that corresponding to the traversal of the upper half. Now the rotation corresponding to each half is equal to $(2n + 1)\pi$ so that the total rotation is $2(2n + 1)\pi$ and the winding number is $2n + 1$.

THEOREM 2. Each continuous function $f : S^2 \to R^2$ maps some pair of antipodal points into the same image point.

Proof: Suppose there exists a map $f : S^2 \to R^2$ such that for each point $P \in S^2$, $f(P) \neq f(-P)$. Let us now identify E^2 with the unit disk in the plane $z = 0$ in R^3. That is, $E^2 = \{(x, y, z) : x^2 + y^2 \leq 1, z = 0\}$. For each point Q in E^2, let Q' be the point in S^2 directly above Q. This means that if $Q = (x, y, 0)$, then $Q' = (x, y, (1 - (x^2 + y^2)^{1/2})$. Notice that if Q is an element of S^1—that is if $x^2 + y^2 = 1$—then $Q' = Q$. Next define a vector distribution W on E^2 by the formula $W(Q) = f(Q') - f(-Q')$. Let V be the restriction of W to S^1. Now since $f(Q') \neq f(-Q')$, we see that W

is a nonzero extension of V to E^2 so that the winding number of V must be zero (Lemma 2). On the other hand, for $Q \in S^1$, $V(Q) = f(Q) - f(-Q) = -V(-Q)$ so that by Lemma 3 the winding number of V must be an odd integer and therefore not equal to zero. This contradiction completes the proof.

EXERCISE

Let f and g be continuous real-valued functions on S^2; that is, $f, g : S^2 \to R^1$. Prove that there exists a point P in S^2 such that $f(P) = f(-P)$ and $g(P) = g(-P)$.

An illustration of the exercise above can be stated as follows. Suppose that the surface of the earth is a sphere and that temperature and barometric pressure are continuous functions. We conclude that, at any instant in time, there exists a pair of antipodal points on the earth's surface at which the temperature readings are equal and the barometric pressure readings are also equal.

EXERCISE

Prove that R^2 and R^3 are not homeomorphic.

In the applications of topological methods to other areas of mathematics, a powerful tool is provided by various fixed-point theorems. In fact it can be argued that any existence theorem is a fixed-point theorem in disguise. For example, a solution of a differential equation is a fixed point under a mapping of a function space. It is easy to see that the fixed-point property is a topological property. Therefore it follows from Theorem 1 that any space homeomorphic to a disk has the fixed-point property.

Theorem 1 is the simplest case of the Brouwer Fixed-Point Theorem. The statement of this theorem involves the higher dimensional analogues of the sets given in Definition 1. In Euclidean space R^{n+1}, the set E^{n+1} is the "solid ball" consisting of all points whose distance from the origin is less than or equal to 1. S^n is the point-set boundary of E^{n+1} and consists of all points in R^{n+1} whose distance from the origin is equal to 1. The Brouwer theorem states that E^{n+1} has the fixed-point property for $n \geq 0$. This is equivalent to the statement that S^n is not a retract of E^{n+1}. There is a generalization of Theorem 2, the Borsuk–Ulam Theorem, which states that any continuous mapping from S^n into R^n maps some pair of antipodal points into the same image point.

The proofs of these theorems use a generalization of the notion of winding number. It is clear that the winding number of a nonzero vector distribution V on S^1 does not depend on the actual lengths of the vectors $V(x, y)$. Therefore, one is led to consider distributions in which each vector has unit length. Such a unit vector distribution on S^1 is precisely a continuous function $V : S^1 \to S^1$. In Chapter III the definition will be given of the *degree* of a map $f : S^n \to S^n$. The degree of the map f is an integer which coincides with the winding number when $n = 1$; it will be shown that f can be extended to E^{n+1} if and only if its degree is zero. This means that the necessary condition given in Lemma 2 is also sufficient.

The geometric ideas used in defining the winding number are inadequate in higher dimensions and a more algebraic approach to the problem is provided by the simplicial homology theory. It is rather surprising that this same theory furnishes easy solutions to a wide variety of problems once considered difficult. For example, an immediate consequence of the Borsuk–Ulam Theorem is that R^m and R^n are not homeomorphic for $m \neq n$.

The more significant contributions of homology theory are of a nonelementary nature and many are completely beyond the range of this book. However, it might be mentioned that the winding number technique used in this introduction can be used to prove that there does not exist a continuous nonzero distribution of *tangent* vectors on S^2. This tells us that at any instant in time there exists a point on the surface of the earth at which the wind is not blowing!

CHAPTER I

THE HOMOLOGY GROUPS OF A COMPLEX

In this chapter we begin the study of the collection of techniques known as "algebraic topology" or "homology theory." Although these techniques will eventually be used in the investigation of topological spaces of a rather general nature, our first applications will be to spaces which are particularly simple subsets of Euclidean n-space R^n. These subsets are those that can be assembled in conformity with a prescribed set of rules from certain elementary "building blocks" called *simplexes*. A set that can be so constructed is called a *polytope*. A particular set of directions for assembling simplexes into a specific polytope is called a *complex*, and the resulting polytope itself is called the *space of the complex*.

In the beginning, then, homology theory will be applicable only to a restricted class of topological spaces called polytopes. There are several methods of enlarging this class of spaces, and these fall into two general categories. In the first place, the rules governing the assembling of simplexes into polytopes can be liberalized. This amounts to generalizing the definition of a complex. Another method is to study spaces which are in some sense limits of polytopes. Properties of the limit spaces can then be deduced by studying the approximating polytopes.

As suggested by the preceding paragraphs, the present chapter will be concerned with the basic definitions of homology theory and certain properties of Euclidean spaces.

1. R^n AS A REAL VECTOR SPACE

Although it will be assumed here that the reader is familiar with the elementary properties of Euclidean space, several basic definitions will be repeated for ease of reference. For example, we have the following definition of Euclidean n-space.

DEFINITION 1. The set R^n (Euclidean n-space) is the totality of ordered n-tuples of real numbers. An element a of R^n is written

$$a = (a^1, a^2, \ldots, a^n)$$

where each a^i is a real number called a *coordinate* of the element a. An element of R^n is called a *point*.

Next there are the familiar operations of addition and scalar multiplication in R^n. If $x = (x^1, x^2, \ldots, x^n)$ and $y = (y^1, y^2, \ldots, y^n)$ are elements of R^n and c is a real number, then $x + y$ and cx are elements of R^n given by

$$x + y = (x^1 + y^1, x^2 + y^2, \ldots, x^n + y^n)$$
$$cx = (cx^1, cx^2, \ldots, cx^n).$$

Under these operations, R^n is an n-dimensional vector space over the field of real numbers.

DEFINITION 2. Let $S = \{a_0, a_1, \ldots, a_k\}$ be a finite subset of R^n. Then $\pi(a_0, a_1, \ldots, a_k)$ or $\pi(S)$ (called the *hyperplane* spanned by S) is the set of all points p of R^n that can be written

$$p = \sum_{i=0}^{k} \lambda^i a_i \qquad \text{where} \qquad \sum_{i=0}^{k} \lambda^i = 1$$

and each λ^i is a real number.

EXAMPLE 1. Let $a_0 = (1, 0)$, $a_1 = (0, 1)$, and $a_2 = (2, -1)$ be points in R^2. It is easy to see that $\pi(a_0, a_1, a_2) = \pi(a_0, a_1)$.

In Example 1 there is a set $S = \{a_0, a_1, a_2\}$ which is contained in the hyperplane spanned by a proper subset $T = \{a_0, a_1\}$. This situation is somewhat analogous to a set of vectors contained in the vector space spanned by a proper subset. In very much the same way, the concept of geometric independence of points corresponds to linear independence of vectors.

DEFINITION 3. A finite subset $S = \{a_0, a_1, \ldots, a_k\}$ of R^n is said to be *geometrically independent* if S is contained in $\pi(T)$ for no proper subset T of S.

In the statement of Theorem 1, the symbol $V(a_0, a_1, \ldots, a_k)$ will be used to indicate the vector space spanned by the set $\{a_0, a_1, \ldots, a_k\}$. The proof of this theorem will be left as an exercise.

THEOREM 1. Let $S_1 = \{a_0, a_1, \ldots, a_k\}$ and $S_2 = \{b_0, b_1, \ldots, b_s\}$ be finite subets of R^n. Then
  (a) $S_1 \subset \pi(S_2)$ implies $\pi(S_1) \subset \pi(S_2)$
  (b) $\pi(S_1) \subset \pi(S_2)$ implies $V(a_1 - a_0, \ldots, a_k - a_0) \subset V(b_1 - b_0, \ldots, b_s - b_0)$.

THEOREM 2. Let $S = \{a_0, a_1, \ldots, a_k\}$ be a finite subset of R^n. The following properties of S are equivalent.
  (a) S is geometrically independent.
  (b) If $T = \{b_0, b_1, \ldots, b_t\}$ and $S \subset \pi(T)$, then $t \geqslant k$.

  (c) $\displaystyle\sum_{i=0}^{k} \lambda^i a_i = 0$ and $\displaystyle\sum_{i=0}^{k} \lambda^i = 0$ imply $\lambda^i = 0$

for each $i = 0, 1, \ldots, k$.

(d) For each element p of $\pi(S)$, there exist *unique* real numbers $\lambda^0, \lambda^1, \ldots, \lambda^k$ such that

$$p = \sum_{i=0}^{k} \lambda^i a_i \quad \text{and} \quad \sum_{i=0}^{k} \lambda^i = 1.$$

(e) The set $\{a_1 - a_0, \ldots, a_k - a_0\}$ is linearly independent.

Proof: that (d) implies (e). If the set $\{a_1 - a_0, \ldots, a_k - a_0\}$ is linearly dependent, we then have for some $s \neq 0$,

$$a_s - a_0 = \sum \lambda^i (a_i - a_0)$$

where the sum is taken over all i not equal to s or 0. Therefore

$$a_s = \sum \lambda^i a_i + (1 - \sum \lambda^i) a_0,$$

and this last equation contradicts the uniqueness hypothesis of part (b). The rest of the proof of Theorem 2 is left as an exercise.

DEFINITION 4. Let $S = \{a_0, a_1, \ldots, a_k\}$ be a geometrically independent subset of R^n. The hyperplane $\pi(S)$ is called a k-dimensional hyperplane. For each element p of $\pi(S)$, the numbers $\lambda^0, \lambda^1, \ldots, \lambda^k$ given in part (d) of Theorem 2 are called the *barycentric coordinates* of the point p relative to the set S. By way of contrast, the coordinates given in Definition 1 are called *Euclidean coordinates*.

As examples of hyperplanes, a 1-dimensional hyperplane is a line, a 2-dimensional hyperplane is a plane, and so forth. The reader will be asked in an exercise to prove that any element p of a hyperplane $\pi(a_0, a_1, \ldots, a_k)$ can be written $p = a_0 + q$ where q is an element of the vector space $V(a_1 - a_0, \ldots, a_k - a_0)$. It will follow that each hyperplane is a "translation" or "coset" of a subspace of R^n.

EXAMPLE 2. In R^3 let $a_1 = (1, 0, 0)$, $a_2 = (0, 1, 0)$, and $a_3 = (0, 0, 1)$. The set $\{a_1, a_2, a_3\}$ is easily seen to be geometrically independent. The 2-dimensional hyperplane $\pi(a_1, a_2, a_3)$ is the set

$$\{(x^1, x^2, x^3) \in R^3 : \sum x^i = 1\}.$$

The barycentric coordinates of a point (x^1, x^2, x^3) in this hyperplane are the numbers x^1, x^2, x^3.

EXERCISE 1

1. Prove Theorem 1.

2. Complete the proof of Theorem 2.

3. Show that for each element p of a hyperplane $\pi(a_0, a_1, \ldots, a_k)$, there exists an element q of the vector space $V(a_1 - a_0, a_2 - a_0, \ldots, a_k - a_0)$ such that $p = a_0 + q$.

4. Consider the following points in the plane R^2:

$$a_0 = (0, 0),\ a_1 = (1, 0),\ a_2 = (0, 1),\ a_3 = (1, 1).$$

Show that the sets $S_1 = \{a_0, a_1, a_2\}$ and $S_2 = \{a_1, a_2, a_3\}$ are geometrically independent. Let p be a point in R^2 with Euclidean coordinates x and y. Express the barycentric coordinates of p with respect to the set S_1 as functions of x and y. Do the same for the set S_2.

5. Let $S = \{a_0, a_1, a_2\}$ be a geometrically independent subset of R^2 and let $\lambda^0, \lambda^1, \lambda^2$ be barycentric coordinates in R^2 with respect to the set S. Show that $\lambda^0 = 1$ is an equation of the line through a_0 parallel to the line containing a_1 and a_2.

6. Let $\{a_0, a_1, a_2, a_3\}$ be a geometrically independent subset of R^3. Find an equation of the plane in R^3 which is parallel to the line $\pi(a_2, a_3)$ and contains the line $\pi(a_0, a_1)$. Find an equation of the plane which contains a_0 and is parallel to the plane $\pi(a_1, a_2, a_3)$.

2. CONTINUITY OF BARYCENTRIC COORDINATES

In Example 2 of Section 1 we had an example of a hyperplane in which the barycentric coordinates of each point with respect to a certain spanning set were the same as the Euclidean coordinates. This suggests that the barycentric coordinates, when considered as real-valued functions on a subset of R^n, are continuous in the ordinary topology of R^n. In this section it will be proved that this is indeed the case.

As a beginning, Theorem 3 will provide a necessary and sufficient condition that a subset $S = \{a_0, a_1, \ldots, a_n\}$ of R^n be geometrically independent. It is easy to see that for such a set containing $n + 1$ elements, $\pi(S) = R^n$. For this particular case, an expression of the barycentric coordinates as functions of the Euclidean coordinates will be given in Theorem 4.

THEOREM 3. Let $S = \{a_0, a_1, \ldots, a_n\}$ be a subset of R^n and, for each i, let $a_i = (a_i^1, a_i^2, \ldots, a_i^n)$. Then the set S is geometrically independent if and only if the determinant

(1)
$$\begin{vmatrix} a_0^1 & a_0^2 & \cdots & a_0^n & 1 \\ a_1^1 & a_1^2 & \cdots & a_1^n & 1 \\ \cdot & \cdot & \cdots & \cdot & \cdot \\ \cdot & \cdot & \cdots & \cdot & \cdot \\ a_n^1 & a_n^2 & \cdots & a_n^n & 1 \end{vmatrix}$$

is not zero.

Proof: By part (c) of Theorem 2, the set S is geometrically dependent if and only if the system of equations

(2)
$$\sum \lambda^i a_i^j = 0, \qquad j = 1, 2, \ldots, n$$
$$\sum \lambda^i = 0$$

has a nontrivial solution vector $(\lambda^0, \lambda^1, \ldots, \lambda^n)$. From this, the proof of the theorem follows easily since the determinant (1) is the determinant of the system (2).

DEFINITION 5. Let $S = \{a_0, a_1, \ldots, a_n\}$ be a subset of R^n. The determinant

$$\begin{vmatrix} a_0^1 & a_0^2 & \cdots & a_0^n & 1 \\ a_1^1 & a_1^2 & \cdots & a_1^n & 1 \\ \cdot & \cdot & \cdots & \cdot & \cdot \\ \cdot & \cdot & \cdots & \cdot & \cdot \\ a_n^1 & a_n^2 & \cdots & a_n^n & 1 \end{vmatrix}$$

is indicated by the symbol $d(S)$.

THEOREM 4. Let $S = \{a_0, a_1, \ldots, a_n\}$ be a geometrically independent subset of R^n, and for each $x = (x^1, x^2, \ldots, x^n)$ in R^n, denote by $\lambda^i(x)$ or λ^i the barycentric coordinates of x with respect to the set S so that

$$x = \sum \lambda^i(x) a_i \qquad \text{and} \qquad \sum \lambda^i(x) = 1.$$

Then $\lambda^i(x) = d^i(x)/d(S)$ where $d^i(x)$ is the determinant obtained by replacing the ith row of $d(S)$ by the vector $(x^1, x^2, \ldots, x^n, 1)$.

Proof: The two equations $x = \sum \lambda^i a_i$ and $\sum \lambda^i = 1$ are equivalent to the system

$$x^j = \sum_{i=0}^{n} \lambda^i a_i^j, \qquad j = 1, 2, \ldots, n$$

$$\sum_{i=0}^{n} \lambda^i = 1.$$

Applying Cramer's rule to this system gives the proof.

As a result of Theorem 4, we see that each barycentric coordinate of a point in R^n with respect to a geometrically independent subset $S = \{a_0, a_1, \ldots, a_n\}$ is a linear function of the Euclidean coordinates and is therefore a continuous real-valued function on R^n. Now suppose that $T = \{a_0, a_1, \ldots, a_k\}$ is a subset of the geometrically independent set S. For each point x of $\pi(T)$ let $\mu^i(x)$ be the barycentric coordinates with respect to the set T, and for each point x of R^n let $\lambda^i(x)$ be the barycentric coordinates with respect to the set S. For each element x of $\pi(T)$, we have $\mu^i(x) = \lambda^i(x)$ and it follows that each $\mu^i(x)$ is a continuous real-valued function defined on $\pi(T)$. To complete the proof that barycentric coordinates are continuous functions, it must be shown that each geometrically independent set in R^n is a subset of a geometrically independent set S such that $\pi(S) = R^n$. This is the content of the next theorem.

THEOREM 5. Let $T = \{a_0, a_1, \ldots, a_k\}$ be a geometrically independent subset of R^n. There exist points $a_{k+1}, a_{k+2}, \ldots, a_n$ of R^n such that the set $S = \{a_0, a_1, \ldots, a_n\}$ is geometrically independent.

Proof: Let T be as in the statement of the theorem. Then by part (e) of Theorem 2, the set $\{a_1 - a_0, \ldots, a_k - a_0\}$ is linearly independent. Consequently, there exist points $b_{k+1}, b_{k+2}, \ldots, b_n$ such that the set

$$\{a_1 - a_0, a_2 - a_0, \ldots, a_k - a_0, b_{k+1}, b_{k+2}, \ldots, b_n\}$$

is a basis of R^n. Now let $a_i = b_i + a_0$ for $i = k + 1, k + 2, \ldots, n$. Then again by part (e) of Theorem 2, the set $S = \{a_0, a_1, \ldots, a_n\}$ is geometrically independent. This completes the proof.

The proof of the next theorem is now immediate.

THEOREM 6. Let $S = \{a_0, a_1, \ldots, a_k\}$ be a geometrically independent subset of R^n, and for each point x of $\pi(a_0, a_1, \ldots, a_k)$ let $\lambda^i(x)$ be the barycentric coordinates of x with respect to the set S. Then each $\lambda^i(x)$ is a continuous real-valued function on $\pi(a_0, a_1, \ldots, a_k)$.

EXERCISE 2

1. Show that the subset $S = \{a_0, a_1, \ldots, a_k\}$ of R^n is geometrically independent if and only if the following matrix has rank $k + 1$.

$$\begin{pmatrix} a_0^1 & a_0^2 & \cdots & a_0^n & 1 \\ a_1^1 & a_1^2 & \cdots & a_1^n & 1 \\ \cdot & \cdot & \cdots & \cdot & \cdot \\ \cdot & \cdot & \cdots & \cdot & \cdot \\ a_k^1 & a_k^2 & \cdots & a_k^n & 1 \end{pmatrix}$$

2. Let $S = \{a_0, a_1, \ldots, a_n\}$ be a geometrically independent subset of R^n. Show that for $k < n$,

$$\pi(a_0, a_1, \ldots, a_k)$$
$$= \bigcap_{i=k+1}^{n} \{x \in R^n : d(a_0, \ldots, a_{i-1}, x, a_{i+1}, \ldots, a_n) = 0\}.$$

3. Use the results of Problem 2 to find equations for the line in R^3 containing the points $(1, 1, 1)$ and $(1, 2, 3)$.

4. Find equations for the plane in R^4 containing the points $(1, 0, 0, 1)$, $(1, 1, 0, 0)$, $(1, 1, 1, 0)$.

5. Let $\{a_0, a_1, \ldots, a_n\}$ be a geometrically independent subset of R^n and let λ^i be barycentric coordinates with respect to this set. Show that $\sum_{i=0}^{k} \lambda^i = 1$ is an equation of the $(n-1)$-dimensional hyperplane in R^n which contains the set $\{a_0, a_1, \ldots, a_k\}$ and is "parallel" to the hyperplane $\pi(a_{k+1}, \ldots, a_n)$.

6. Prove that any subset of a k-dimensional hyperplane containing $k + 2$ points is geometrically dependent.

3. SIMPLEXES AND COMPLEXES IN R^n

The simplex spanned by a geometrically independent set S is the subset of the hyperplane $\pi(S)$ given by the following definition.

DEFINITION 6. Let $S = \{a_0, a_1, \ldots, a_k\}$ be a geometrically independent subset of R^n. Then $\Delta(S)$ or $\Delta(a_0, a_1, \ldots, a_k)$ (called the *simplex spanned by* S) is the set of all points p of R^n that can be written

$$p = \sum_{i=0}^{k} \lambda^i a_i, \qquad \sum_{i=0}^{k} \lambda^i = 1, \qquad \lambda^i > 0 \text{ for } i = 0, 1, \ldots, k.$$

According to Definition 6, $\Delta(S)$ consists of those points of $\pi(S)$ whose barycentric coordinates with respect to S are all positive. The set $\Delta(S)$ is called a k-dimensional simplex or just a k-simplex. Also, the symbol s^k is frequently used to represent a k-simplex, the purpose of the superscript being to emphasize the dimension of the simplex. Each point a_i is a *vertex* of the simplex $\Delta(a_0, a_1, \ldots, a_k)$. If each vertex of s^t is also a vertex of s^k, then s^t is a t-dimensional *face* of s^k, and $s^t < s^k$ is written. Each vertex of s^k is a 0-dimensional face of s^k. We agree that the null set $\varnothing$ is a (-1)-dimensional face of every simplex. Any face of s^k other than $\varnothing$ and s^k itself is called a proper face of s^k.

A 0-dimensional simplex is a single point in R^n, and a 1-dimensional simplex is an open line interval. Higher dimensional simplexes may be thought of as generalized line intervals or triangles. A 2-simplex is a triangle, a 3-simplex is a tetrahedron, and so forth.

For each geometrically independent subset S of R^n, the simplex $\Delta(S)$ is an open set in the relative topology of the hyperplane $\pi(S)$. To see that this is so, let λ^i be the barycentric coordinates of points in $\pi(S)$ relative to S and for each $i = 0, 1, \ldots, k$ define G_i to be the set of all points of $\pi(S)$ for which $\lambda^i(x) > 0$. Because of the continuity of the functions λ^i, each G_i is open in $\pi(S)$. Also, $\Delta(S) = \cap\{G_i\}$, and therefore $\Delta(S)$ is open in $\pi(S)$. For this reason, a simplex as given in Definition 6 is sometimes called an open simplex. The closure of a simplex is called a closed simplex. Observe that the closure of $\Delta(S)$ in $\pi(S)$ coincides with the closure in R^n.

THEOREM 7. If a simplex s^r is a face of a simplex s^k, then s^r is contained in the closure of s^k. Conversely, each point in the closure of s^k is an element of a unique face of s^k.

Proof: Let $S = \{a_0, a_1, \ldots, a_k\}$ be the set of vertices of s^k. Then the closure of s^k consists of those points of $\pi(S)$ all of whose barycentric coordinates with respect to S are nonnegative. Suppose now that $x \in s^r <$ s^k. It follows that the barycentric coordinates of x corresponding to vertices of s^r are positive and the remaining coordinates are zero. Therefore all barycentric coordinates are nonnegative and x is an element of the closure of s^k. For the converse, suppose that x is an element of the closure of s^k. Define s^r to be the simplex spanned by those vertices of s^k corresponding to positive barycentric coordinates of x. By definition, x is an element of s^r and it is clear that this is the only face of s^k containing the point x. This completes the proof.

Simplexes in R^n are used as "building blocks" for other sets, and subsets of R^n that can be built up from these blocks in a specified way will now be studied. The following definition is more precise.

DEFINITION 7. A *complex* in R^n is a finite set K of nonnull simplexes in R^n having these properties.

(a) If s^k and s^t are distinct elements of K, then $s^k \cap s^t = \varnothing$.

(b) If s^k is an element of K and s^t is a proper face of s^k, then s^t is an element of K.

If m is the maximum dimension of simplexes in K, then K is said to have dimension m. We then write $\dim(K) = m$ and say that K is an m-complex. The *space* of K, written $|K|$, is the set $\cup \{s^k : s^k \in K\}$. A subset of R^n is called a *polytope* if it is the space of some complex. A complex K is called a *triangulation* of the polytope $|K|$.

EXAMPLE 3. If s^r and s^t are distinct faces of a simplex s^k, then by Theorem 7, $s^r \cap s^t = \varnothing$. It follows that the collection $\widehat{K_1}$ of all nonnull faces of s^k is a complex. This complex is called the *combinatorial closure* of s^k. The set K_2 of all proper faces of s^k is a complex called the *combinatorial boundary* of s^k. By Theorem 7, the polytope $|K_1|$ is the point-set closure of s^k, and it will be left as an exercise to prove that $|K_2|$ is the point-set boundary of s^k in the hyperplane spanned by the vertices of s^k.

The word "combinatorial" used in connection with Example 3 is a relic from an earlier age.

In the next example we have two distinct triangulations of the same polytope.

EXAMPLE 4. In R^2, let $a_0 = (0, 0)$, $a_1 = (1, 0)$, $a_2 = (1, 1)$, and $a_3 = (0, 1)$. Let K_1 be the complex consisting of all nonnull faces of the simplexes $\Delta(a_0, a_1, a_2)$ and $\Delta(a_0, a_2, a_3)$. Let K_2 be the complex consisting of the nonnull faces of the simplexes $\Delta(a_0, a_1, a_3)$ and $\Delta(a_1, a_2, a_3)$. Then $|K_1| = |K_2|$.

We now come to a concept upon which much of our future work will depend. The notion of an *oriented simplex* is a generalization of the idea of a directed line segment. A line interval can be directed or oriented in just two ways. A natural method of specifying one of the two possible orientations of a line segment is to list its vertices (endpoints) in one of the two possible orders. A modification of this method can be used to orient a triangle. The difference now is that, whereas there are only two permutations of the vertices of a line interval, there are six permutations of the vertices of a triangle. However, even in the case of a triangle, there are only two distinct cyclic permutations, and each of these corresponds to an orientation of the triangle. If a_0, a_1, and a_2 are the vertices, then the cyclic permutations (a_0, a_1, a_2), (a_1, a_2, a_0), and (a_2, a_0, a_1) are the same. Intuitively, an orientation of a triangle can be thought of as a prescribed manner of traversing the boundary.

To extend this idea to a simplex of arbitrary dimension, we proceed as follows. If the $k + 1$ vertices of a k-simplex Δ are written down in an arbitrary order, then each of the $(k + 1)!$ possible orders is either an even or an odd permutation of the original order. Two orders are said to be *equivalent* if they are both even or both odd permutations of the original order. In this way, the set of all orders is decomposed into two equivalence classes each containing $(k + 1)!/2$ elements. These equivalence classes are independent of the original arbitrary order and each represents an orientation of the simplex Δ. A formal definition now follows.

DEFINITION 8. An *oriented simplex* is a pair consisting of (1) a simplex Δ, and (2) one of the two equivalence classes of orders of the vertices of Δ.

In order to specify an oriented simplex, it is necessary to select one of the two equivalence classes of orders of the vertices of a simplex Δ. When this has been done, we say that Δ has been assigned an orientation. To assign an orientation to Δ it is sufficient to list the vertices in some order since the listed order is an element of one of the two equivalence classes. If Δ is a simplex with vertices $a_0, a_1, \ldots, a_k$, then the symbol $\langle a_0, a_1, \ldots, a_k \rangle$ is used to denote the oriented simplex determined by the indicated order. Each of the two oriented simplexes arising from a simplex s^r is said to be the negative of the other. For example, if a_0 and a_1 are points in R^n, then the directed segments $\langle a_0, a_1 \rangle$ and $\langle a_1, a_0 \rangle$ are negatives of each other. Neither of these directed segments is designated as the positive segment, but each is the negative of the other and then $\langle a_0, a_1 \rangle = -\langle a_1, a_0 \rangle$ and $\langle a_1, a_0 \rangle = -\langle a_0, a_1 \rangle$.

Since an orientation of a simplex is an equivalence class of orders of its vertices, there is only one possible orientation of a 0-simplex, consisting as it does of a single vertex. For this reason, the term "oriented simplex" will always mean either a 0-simplex or a simplex of positive dimension with an assigned orientation.

EXERCISE 3

1. Prove that a hyperplane in R^n is a closed set in R^n.

2. Show that the combinatorial closure of a k-simplex is a collection of $2^{k+1} - 1$ simplexes.

3. Let $s^k = \Delta(a_0, a_1, \ldots, a_k)$ be a k-simplex in R^n. Let the matrix A be given by

$$A = \begin{pmatrix} a_0^1 & a_1^1 & \cdots & a_k^1 \\ a_0^2 & a_1^2 & \cdots & a_k^2 \\ \cdot & \cdot\ \cdot & \cdots & \cdot \\ \cdot & \cdot\ \cdot & \cdots & \cdot \\ a_0^n & a_1^n & \cdots & a_k^n \end{pmatrix}$$

Also, let $T: R^{k+1} \to R^n$ be the linear transformation given by $T(x) = Ax$ for $x \in R^{k+1}$ (the element x is considered to be a column vector here). Show that the closure of s^k is the image in R^n under T of the set

$$\{(x^0, x^1, \ldots, x^k) \in R^{k+1} : \sum x^i = 1, x^i \geqslant 0\}.$$

Conclude that each closed simplex (and therefore each polytope in R^n) is a compact subset of R^n.

4. Prove that if K is the combinatorial boundary of a simplex s^n in R^n, then $|K|$ is the point-set boundary of s^n in R^n.

4. CHAIN GROUPS

The idea of orienting a simplex has a natural extension to complexes. If each positive dimensional simplex of a complex K has been assigned an orientation, then K is said to be an *oriented complex*. A symbol such as α will be used to denote a particular mode of orienting a complex K, and the symbol K^α will represent the corresponding oriented complex. The complex K is called the *underlying complex* of the oriented complex K^α, and K^α is called an orientation of the complex K. A complex may be oriented by assigning, in a completely arbitrary fashion, an orientation to each of its simplexes. If K^α and K^β are orientations of the same underlying complex and s^r is a simplex of this complex, then the symbol $f_{\alpha\beta}(s^r)$ is defined to represent the number $+1$ if α and β assign the same orientation to s^r, and $f_{\alpha\beta}(s^r) = -1$ if not. As basic relations among these numbers we have

$$f_{\alpha\alpha}(s^r) = +1$$

(3)
$$f_{\alpha\beta}(s^r) = f_{\beta\alpha}(s^r)$$

$$f_{\alpha\beta}(s^r)f_{\beta\gamma}(s^r) = f_{\alpha\gamma}(s^r).$$

Historically, algebraic topology has its origins in the study of certain "homology groups" defined for each complex K. The next definition will be the first step in the construction of these groups.

DEFINITION 9. Let K^α be an oriented complex, and let G be an additively written abelian group. An *r-dimensional chain* of K^α over G is a function c^α which assigns to each oriented r-simplex of K^α an element of the group G.

When a simplex s^r has been assigned an orientation, then s^r can be called the underlying simplex of the resulting oriented simplex. If c^α is an r-dimensional chain of an oriented complex K^α over a group G, then the symbol $c^\alpha(s^r)$ represents the element of the group G assigned by c^α to the oriented simplex whose underlying simplex is s^r.

DEFINITION 10. The set of r-dimensional chains of an oriented complex K^α over a group G is indicated by the symbol $C_r(K^\alpha; G)$.

This set is closed under functional addition. The sum of two chains is given by

(4) $$(c_1^\alpha + c_2^\alpha)(s^r) = c_1^\alpha(s^r) + c_2^\alpha(s^r).$$

THEOREM 8. The set $C_r(K^\alpha; G)$ is a commutative group under the addition given in Definition 10.

If K^α and K^β are orientations of the same complex K and c^α and c^β are r-dimensional chains of K^α and K^β, respectively, over the same group G, then c^α is defined to be *chain-equivalent* to c^β provided that for each r-simplex s^r of K it is true that $c^\alpha(s^r) = f_{\alpha\beta}(s^r)c^\beta(s^r)$. It follows from the properties of the numbers $f_{\alpha\beta}(s^r)$ that the relation so defined is actually an equivalence. The next definition is given in terms of this relation.

DEFINITION 11. Let K^α be an orientation of a complex K and let c^α be an r-dimensional chain of K^α over an abelian group G. The chain-equivalence class of c^α is called an *r-dimensional chain* of K over G. The set of r-dimensional chains of K over G is indicated by the symbol $C_r(K; G)$.

An r-dimensional chain of a complex K (in contrast to a chain of an *oriented* complex) is usually designated by a lower case letter such as c without a notational device indicating a particular orientation. The notation c^r is frequently used for a chain of a complex, the purpose of the superscript here being to emphasize the dimension of the chain. It should be observed that a chain of a complex is an equivalence class of chains of oriented complexes. If c^α is in the chain-equivalence class c, then c^α is called a representative of the chain c. The proof of the next theorem is left as an exercise.

THEOREM 9. Let c be an r-dimensional chain of a complex K over a group G. For each orientation K^α of K, there exists exactly one chain c^α of K^α such that c^α is a representative of c.

In making computations involving chains of a complex, one always works with representative chains of oriented complexes. This requires that each result be shown to be independent of the orientation chosen. The first instance of this occurs in defining the sum of two chains. The idea is to define, for each pair c_1 and c_2 of r-dimensional chains of a complex K over a group G, the chain $c_1 + c_2$ of K over G to be the chain-equivalence class of $c_1^\alpha + c_2^\alpha$ where c_1^α and c_2^α are chains of an orientation K^α of K representing c_1 and c_2. The next theorem shows that this definition of sum is "orientation invariant."

THEOREM 10. If K^α and K^β are orientations of a complex K, and c_1^α, c_2^α, c_1^β, c_2^β are r-dimensional chains of K^α and K^β with c_1^α equivalent to c_1^β and c_2^α equivalent to c_2^β, then $c_1^\alpha + c_2^\alpha$ is equivalent to $c_1^\beta + c_2^\beta$.

Proof: For each simplex s^r of K, we have

$$(c_1^\alpha + c_2^\alpha)(s^r) = c_1^\alpha(s^r) + c_2^\alpha(s^r)$$
$$= f_{\alpha\beta}(s^r)c_1^\beta(s^r) + f_{\alpha\beta}(s^r)c_2^\beta(s^r)$$
$$= f_{\alpha\beta}(s^r)\{c_1^\beta(s^r) + c_2^\beta(s^r)\} = f_{\alpha\beta}(s^r)(c_1^\beta + c_2^\beta)(s^r).$$

Theorem 10 permits us to make the formal definition of the sum of two chains.

DEFINITION 12. If c_1 and c_2 are r-dimensional chains of a complex K over a group G, then the sum $c_1 + c_2$ is defined to be the equivalence class of $c_1^\alpha + c_2^\alpha$ where α is an orientation of K and c_1^α and c_2^α are representatives of c_1 and c_2.

THEOREM 11. The set $C_r(K; G)$ of r-dimensional chains of the complex K over the group G is an abelian group under the addition given in Definition 12. For each orientation K^α of K, the group $C_r(K; G)$ is isomorphic to $C_r(K^\alpha; G)$.

The proof of Theorem 11 is left as an exercise.

The group $C_r(K; G)$ is called the group of r-dimensional chains of K over G. An element of this group is frequently called simply an r-chain. If the complex K has no r-simplexes for some dimension r, then we agree that the group $C_r(K; G)$ contains a single element and write $C_r(K; G) = 0$. The group G used in this construction is called the coefficient group.

EXERCISE 4

1. Prove Theorem 8.

2. Prove Theorem 9.

3. Prove Theorem 11.

4. Let K be the combinatorial closure of an n-simplex. Prove that for $r > n$, $C_r(K; G) = 0$ for each coefficient group G and that $C_n(K; G)$ is isomorphic to G.

5. Prove that if a complex K contains m simplexes of dimension r, then $C_r(K; G)$ is isomorphic to $G \oplus \cdots \oplus G$ for m summands.

6. For each complex K let $\bar{K}$ be the set whose elements are (1) the 0-simplexes of K and (2) the oriented simplexes arising from the simplexes of K. Thus for each positive dimensional simplex s^r of K, the set $\bar{K}$ contains two elements, namely the two oriented simplexes arising from s^r. A function c mapping the oriented r-simplexes of $\bar{K}$ into an additive group G is said to be *skew symmetric* provided $c(s^r) = -c(-s^r)$ whenever s^r and $-s^r$ are opposite orientations of the same simplex. Prove that the set $\bar{C}_r(K; G)$ of such skew symmetric functions is a group under functional addition and that this group is isomorphic to $C_r(K; G)$.

5. INCIDENCE NUMBERS

In this section we wish to define an *incidence number*, indicated by the symbol $[s^r, s^{r-1}]^\alpha$, for each complex K, for each pair of simplexes s^r and s^{r-1} of K whose dimensions differ by one, and for each orientation K^α of K.

The following notation will be convenient here and in later material. If $s^r = \langle a_0, a_1, \ldots, a_r \rangle$ is an r-simplex, then the $(r-1)$-dimensional face of s^r obtained by omitting the ith vertex a_i is indicated by the symbol $\langle a_0, \ldots, \hat{a}_i, \ldots, a_r \rangle$.

An orientation of an r-simplex s^r determines an orientation of each $(r-1)$-dimensional face of s^r in the following manner. If the orientation of s^r is given by $s^r = \langle a_0, a_1, \ldots, a_r \rangle$ and s^{r-1} is the face obtained by omitting the vertex a_i, then the orientation *inherited* by s^{r-1} from s^r is given by

$$s^{r-1} = (-1)^i \langle a_0, \ldots, \hat{a}_i, \ldots, a_r \rangle.$$

Now let s^r and s^{r-1} be simplexes of a complex K. First of all, if s^{r-1} is not a face of s^r, then the incidence number $[s^r, s^{r-1}]^\alpha$ is defined to be zero for each orientation α. Next, suppose that s^{r-1} is a face of s^r and that α is an orientation of K. Consider now two ways of assigning an orientation to s^{r-1}. First, α assigns an orientation directly to s^{r-1} and second, s^{r-1} inherits an orientation from the orientation assigned by α to s^r. If these two orientations of s^{r-1} are the same, the incidence number $[s^r, s^{r-1}]^\alpha$ is defined to be $+1$; otherwise its value is -1.

THEOREM 12. If s^r and s^{r-1} are simplexes of a complex K, and K^α and K^β are orientations of K, then

$$[s^r, s^{r-1}]^\alpha = f_{\alpha\beta}(s^r)f_{\alpha\beta}(s^{r-1})[s^r, s^{r-1}]^\beta.$$

The proof is left as an exercise.

THEOREM 13. $\sum_i [s^r, s_i^{r-1}]^\alpha [s_i^{r-1}, s^{r-2}]^\alpha = 0.$

In the statement of Theorem 13 it is assumed that s^r and s^{r-2} are fixed simplexes in a complex K, that α is a fixed orientation of K, and that the sum is taken over all simplexes in K of dimension $r-1$. The first step in the proof is to observe that if β is also an orientation of K, then by Theorem 12 we have

$$\sum_i [s^r, s_i^{r-1}]^\alpha [s_i^{r-1}, s^{r-2}]^\alpha = f_{\alpha\beta}(s^r)f_{\alpha\beta}(s^{r-2}) \sum_i [s^r, s_i^{r-1}]^\beta [s_i^{r-1}, s^{r-2}]^\beta.$$

This result shows that the truth of the theorem does not depend on the particular orientation α.

Consider now the case in which s^{r-2} is a face of s^r. This means that s^{r-2} is the simplex obtained from s^r by omitting two vertices, a_i and a_j. In this case there are exactly two $(r-1)$-simplexes s_1^{r-1} and s_2^{r-1} such that $s^{r-2} < s_i^{r-1} < s^r$ and these are obtained from s^r by omitting in turn the vertices a_i and a_j. By renumbering the vertices we may arrange that $a_i = a_0$ and $a_j = a_1$. Let us choose an orientation β of K that assigns the following orientations to $s^r, s_1^{r-1}, s_2^{r-1}$, and s^{r-2}.

$$s^r = \langle a_0, a_1, \ldots, a_r \rangle$$
$$s_1^{r-1} = \langle a_0, a_2, \ldots, a_r \rangle$$
$$s_2^{r-1} = \langle a_1, a_2, \ldots, a_r \rangle$$
$$s^{r-2} = \langle a_2, \ldots, a_r \rangle$$

By direct calculation we see that $[s^r, s_1^{r-1}]^\beta [s_1^{r-1}, s^{r-2}]^\beta = -1$, and $[s^r, s_2^{r-1}]^\beta [s_2^{r-1}, s^{r-2}]^\beta = +1$ so that the theorem is true for the orientation K^β and therefore for any orientation K^α.

To complete the proof, we observe that if s^{r-2} is not a face of s^r, then the product $[s^r, s_i^{r-1}]^\alpha [s_i^{r-1}, s^{r-2}]^\alpha$ is equal to zero for each s_i^{r-1}; hence the theorem is true for this case.

6. BOUNDING CHAINS AND CYCLES

A chain of a complex or of an oriented complex over the additive group Z of integers is called an *integral* chain. The coefficient group Z is particularly important in the theory of chain groups. In part, this importance is due to the possibility of defining a " multiplication" of an integral chain by an element of an arbitrary abelian group. This multiplication assigns a chain gc of K over G to each pair consisting of an integral chain c of the complex K and an element g of the group G. The actual definition is as follows. For each orientation K^α of K, define the chain $(gc)^\alpha$ of K^α over G by

$$(gc)^\alpha(s^r) = (c^\alpha(s^r)) \cdot g.$$

The symbol $(c^\alpha(s^r)) \cdot g$ here represents an integral multiple of the group element g. If K^β is also an orientation of K, then $(gc)^\alpha$ is equivalent to $(gc)^\beta$ since we have

$$\begin{aligned} (gc)^\alpha(s^r) &= (c^\alpha(s^r)) \cdot g \\ &= f_{\alpha\beta}(s^r) c^\beta(s^r) \cdot g \\ &= f_{\alpha\beta}(s^r)(gc)^\beta(s^r). \end{aligned}$$

The chain gc is now defined to be the chain-equivalence class of $(gc)^\alpha$ and the remarks just made show that this definition is orientation-invariant.

Next, suppose that K^α is an orientation of a complex K and that s_j^r is an orientated simplex in K^α. Associated with this particular oriented simplex is the integral r-chain $(\sigma_j^r)^\alpha$ of K^α given by

$$(5) \qquad (\sigma_j^r)^\alpha(s_i^r) = \begin{cases} 1 & \text{if } i = j \\ 0 & \text{if } i \neq j. \end{cases}$$

In other words $(\sigma_j^r)^\alpha(s_i^r) = \delta_{ij}$ where the symbol δ_{ij} is defined by

$$\delta_{ij} = \begin{cases} 1 & \text{if } i = j \\ 0 & \text{if } i \neq j. \end{cases}$$

A chain defined in this manner is called an *elementary* integral r-chain of K^α. Observe that there is a one-to-one correspondence between the oriented r-simplexes of K^α and the elementary integral r-chains of K^α. This correspondence is the justification of the custom of using the symbol s_i^r to indicate both an oriented simplex and the corresponding elementary integral r-chain. Such dual usage can be employed only after a definite orientation has been assigned to the complex K. The chain-equivalence class of an elementary integral r-chain of K^α is called an elementary integral r-chain of K. If $(\sigma_j^r)^\alpha$ is defined by (5), then the chain $-(\sigma_j^r)^\alpha$ is not an elementary integral r-chain of K^α although its equivalence class is an elementary integral r-chain of K.

THEOREM 14. Each r-chain c^α of $C_r(K^\alpha; G)$ can be written uniquely in the form

$$c^\alpha = \sum_j g_j^\alpha(\sigma_j^r)^\alpha$$

where $\{(\sigma_j^r)^\alpha\}$ are the elementary integral r-chains of K^α and each g_j^α is an element of G.

Proof: The values of the chain

$$\sum_j g_j^\alpha(\sigma_j^r)^\alpha$$

are given by

$$\left(\sum_j g_j^\alpha(\sigma_j^r)^\alpha\right)(s_i^r) = \sum_j g_j^\alpha((\sigma_j^r)^\alpha(s_i^r)) = \sum_j g_j^\alpha \, \delta_{ji} = g_i^\alpha.$$

Consequently,

$$c^\alpha = \sum_j g_j^\alpha(\sigma_j^r)^\alpha$$

if and only if $g_j^\alpha = c^\alpha(s_j^r)$ for each j.

The theorem just established provides two equivalent ways of specifying the values of an r-chain of K^α, namely

(6) $$c^\alpha(s_j^r) = g_j^\alpha \qquad \text{for each } j,$$

(7) $$c^\alpha = \sum_j g_j^\alpha(\sigma_j^r)^\alpha.$$

This result will be useful in the next construction.

The task is now to define an operator ∂ which assigns to each r-chain ($r > 0$) an ($r - 1$)-chain called its *boundary*. The first step is to define, for each r-chain

$$c^\alpha = \sum_j g_j^\alpha (\sigma_j^r)^\alpha$$

of K^α over G, the boundary of c^α (indicated by ∂c^α) to be the ($r - 1$)-chain of K^α over G given by

$$\partial c^\alpha = \sum_k \left(\sum_j [s_j^r, s_k^{r-1}]^\alpha g_j^\alpha \right) (\sigma_k^{r-1})^\alpha$$

or equivalently by

$$\partial c^\alpha (s_k^{r-1}) = \sum_j [s_j^r, s_k^{r-1}]^\alpha g_j^\alpha.$$

In the special case when c^α is the elementary integral r-chain given by $s^r = \langle a_0, a_1, \ldots, a_r \rangle$, the last equation reduces to the following useful formula.

(8) $\partial \langle a_0, a_1, \ldots, a_r \rangle = \sum_i (-1)^i \langle a_0, \ldots, \hat{a}_i, \ldots, a_r \rangle.$

Next we wish to define the boundary of an r-chain c of the (unoriented) complex K over G as the equivalence class of ∂c^α where c^α is any representative of c. The necessary invariance theorem is the next proposition.

THEOREM 15. If c^α is chain-equivalent to c^β, then ∂c^α is chain-equivalent to ∂c^β.

Proof: Let

$$c^\alpha = \sum_j g_j^\alpha (\sigma_j^r)^\alpha \qquad \text{and} \qquad c^\beta = \sum_j g_j^\beta (\sigma_j^r)^\beta.$$

Then

$$g_j^\beta = c^\beta (s_j^r) = f_{\alpha\beta}(s_j^r) c^\alpha (s_j^r) = f_{\alpha\beta}(s_j^r) g_j^\alpha$$

so that

$$(\partial c^\beta)(s_k^{r-1}) = \sum_j [s_j^r, s_k^{r-1}]^\beta g_j^\beta$$

$$= \sum_j f_{\alpha\beta}^2 (s_j^r) f_{\alpha\beta}(s_k^{r-1}) [s_j^r, s_k^{r-1}]^\alpha g_j^\alpha = f_{\alpha\beta}(s_k^{r-1})(\partial c^\alpha)(s_k^{r-1}).$$

We may now state the formal definition of the boundary operator ∂.

DEFINITION 13. The boundary of an r-chain c in $C_r(K; G)$ $(r > 0)$ is defined to be the chain-equivalence class of ∂c^α where c^α is any representative of c. The boundary of c is indicated by the symbol ∂c.

Two basic properties of the operator ∂ are given in the next theorem.

THEOREM 16. (a) The operator ∂ is a homomorphism

$$\partial : C_r(K; G) \to C_{r-1}(K; G)\ (r > 0).$$

(b) For any r-chain c, $\partial\partial(c) = 0\ (r > 1)$.

Proof of (b): Let $c^\alpha = \sum_j g_j^\alpha(\sigma_j^r)^\alpha$ be an element of $C_r(K^\alpha; G)$. Then

$$\partial c^\alpha = \sum_k \left(\sum_j g_j^\alpha[s_j^r, s_k^{r-1}]^\alpha \right)(\sigma_k^{r-1})^\alpha$$

$$\partial\partial c^\alpha = \sum_i \sum_k \sum_j g_j^\alpha[s_j^r, s_k^{r-1}]^\alpha[s_k^{r-1}, s_i^{r-2}]^\alpha(\sigma_i^{r-2})^\alpha.$$

It now follows by Theorem 13 that $\partial\partial(c^\alpha) = 0$ and the proof is complete.

DEFINITION 14. If c is an element of $C_r(K; G)\ (r > 0)$ and $\partial(c) = 0$, then c is called a *cycle*. If $c = \partial(c')$ for some chain c' in $C_{r+1}(K; G)$, then by the preceding theorem, c is a cycle and is called a *bounding* cycle of a *boundary*. The set of cycles in $C_r(K; G)$ is the kernel of the homomorphism $\partial : C_r(K; G) \to C_{r-1}(K; G)$ and is denoted by $Z_r(K; G)$. The set of bounding cycles is the image of the homomorphism $\partial : C_{r+1}(K; G) \to C_r(K; G)$ and is denoted by $B_r(K; G)$.

THEOREM 17. $Z_r(K; G)$ and $B_r(K; G)$ are subgroups of $C_r(K; G)$ and $B_r(K; G)$ is contained in $Z_r(K; G)$.

DEFINITION 15. The factor group

$$Z_r(K; G)/B_r(K; G) = H_r(K; G)$$

is called the r-dimensional *homology* group of K over G.

Two cycles z_1 and z_2 in $Z_r(K; G)$ are said to be homologous if they are in the same coset of $B_r(K; G)$. For this reason, the elements of $H_r(K; G)$ are often called r-dimensional homology classes.

7. ABSTRACT COMPLEXES

The present section is a digression and its purpose is to present a method of constructing examples of complexes.

DEFINITION 16. An *abstract complex* K is a finite set of elements $\{a_0, a_1, \ldots, a_m\}$ called vertices together with a collection of subsets called simplexes satisfying the following conditions.

(1) Each set $\{a_i\}$ consisting of a single vertex is a simplex.

(2) Every subset of a simplex is a simplex.

In order to distinguish between types of complexes, those defined earlier may be called *geometric* complexes.

DEFINITION 17. Two complexes K_1 and K_2 (abstract or geometric) are said to be *isomorphic* provided there exists a bijective function $f: K_1^0 \to K_2^0$ from the vertices of K_1 to the vertices of K_2 having the property that a subset $\{a_{i_0}, a_{i_1}, \ldots, a_{i_r}\}$ of K_1^0 is the set of vertices of a simplex in K_1 if and only if $\{f(a_{i_0}), f(a_{i_1}), \ldots, f(a_{i_r})\}$ is the set of vertices of a simplex in K_2. If an abstract complex K_1 is isomorphic to a geometric complex K_2, then K_2 is said to be a *realization* of K_1.

THEOREM 18. Every abstract complex K_1 has a realization K_2 in some Euclidean space R^m.

Proof: Let $\{a_0, a_1, \ldots, a_m\}$ be the vertices of the abstract complex K_1. In Euclidean space R^m consider a simplex $s^m = \Delta(b_0, b_1, \ldots, b_m)$. The complex K_2 is taken to be the subcomplex of the combinatorial closure of s^m given by the rule: $\Delta(b_{i_0}, b_{i_1}, \ldots, b_{i_r})$ is in K_2 if and only if $\{a_{i_0}, a_{i_1}, \ldots, a_{i_r}\}$ is a simplex in K_1. It is now clear that the function $f: K_1^0 \to K_2^0$ given by $f(a_i) = b_i$ is an isomorphism.

EXAMPLE 5. (The 2-dimensional torus) In order to exhibit a 2-complex whose space is homeomorphic to the 2-dimensional torus T^2, we use the familiar process of identifying certain edges of a plane polygonal region. Recall that the torus T^2 is homeomorphic to the quotient space obtained by identifying opposite edges of a rectangle. In the diagram given here, the opposite

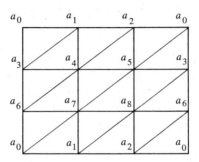

edges of the rectangle have been identified as have the corresponding points on these edges. Thus the diagram describes an abstract complex K_1 having nine vertices, 27 1-simplexes, and 18 2-simplexes. Now let K_2 be a realization of K_1 and we have that the space of K_2 is homeomorphic to the torus T^2.

EXAMPLE 6. (The Klein bottle) This time the opposite edges of the rectangle are identified with the orientations of the vertical edges reversed. Again there are nine vertices, 27 1-simplexes, and 18 2-simplexes.

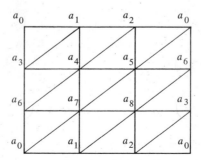

EXAMPLE 7. (The projective plane) A model of the projective plane P^2 is obtained by identifying diametrically opposite points on the boundary of a plane disk. The diagram shown here describes a 2-complex whose space is homeomorphic to P^2. There are six vertices, 15 1-simplexes, and 10 2-simplexes.

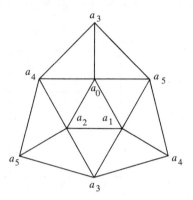

DEFINITION 18. An n-dimensional *pseudomanifold* is an n-complex with the following properties.

(a) Each simplex is a face of an n-simplex.

(b) Each $(n-1)$-simplex is a face of exactly two n-simplexes.

(c) For each pair t_1^n and t_2^n of distinct n-simplexes, there exists a finite sequence $s_1^n, s_1^{n-1}, \ldots, s_{k-1}^{n-1}, s_k^n$ of simplexes such that $s_1^n = t_1^n$, $s_k^n = t_2^n$, and for $1 \leqslant i < k$, each s_i^{n-1} is a face of both s_i^n and s_{i+1}^n.

If there exists an orientation K^α of an n-dimensional pseudomanifold K such that each $(n-1)$-simplex inherits opposite orientations from the two incident n-simplexes, then K is said to be *orientable*. If no such orientation K^α exist, then K is said to be *nonorientable*.

EXERCISE 5

1. Prove Theorem 12.

2. Prove Theorem 16 (a).

3. Consider the complex K consisting of the nonnull faces of a 3-simplex s^3. Let K be oriented as follows.

$$s^3 = \langle a_0, a_1, a_2, a_3 \rangle \quad s_1^2 = \langle a_1, a_2, a_3 \rangle \quad s_1^1 = \langle a_0, a_1 \rangle$$
$$s_2^2 = \langle a_2, a_0, a_3 \rangle \quad s_2^1 = \langle a_0, a_2 \rangle$$
$$s_3^2 = \langle a_0, a_1, a_3 \rangle \quad s_3^1 = \langle a_0, a_3 \rangle$$
$$s_4^2 = \langle a_1, a_0, a_2 \rangle \quad s_4^1 = \langle a_1, a_2 \rangle$$
$$s_5^1 = \langle a_1, a_3 \rangle$$
$$s_6^1 = \langle a_2, a_3 \rangle$$

Verify the following statements.

Each element c of $C_3(K; Z)$ is of the form $c = ns^3$.

$$\partial(ns^3) = n(s_1^2 + s_2^2 + s_3^2 + s_4^2).$$
$$Z_3(K; Z) = 0. \qquad \partial(s_1^2 + s_2^2 + s_3^2 + s_4^2) = 0.$$
$$B_2(K; Z) = Z_2(K; Z). \qquad H_2(K; Z) = 0.$$

4. Let L be the oriented complex consisting of all proper faces of the oriented complex in Problem 3.
Verify: $Z_2(L; Z) \approx Z$, $B_2(L; Z) = 0$, $H_2(L; Z) \approx Z$.

5. Show that the torus T^2 of Example 5 and the combinatorial boundary of a 3-simplex are orientable pseudomanifolds.

6. Show that the Klein bottle and the projective plane are nonorientable pseudomanifolds.

7. A "pinched torus" is obtained by shrinking one longitudinal circle of a torus to a point. Find a complex whose space is homeomorphic to a pinched torus and show that this is an orientable 2-dimensional pseudomanifold.

8. THE ZERO-DIMENSIONAL GROUPS

In the discussion thus far of cycles and bounding cycles it has been assumed that the chains involved were of positive dimension since it is clear that some special definition is needed for the boundary of a 0-chain. The simplest possible definition is to set the boundary of each 0-dimensional chain to be zero. This is consistent with the earlier convention because $C_q(K; G) = 0$ whenever a complex K contains no simplexes of a certain dimension q. With this in mind, it is natural to define $C_q(K; G)$ as the zero group for each negative dimension q. The homomorphism

$$\partial : C_0(K; G) \to C_{-1}(K; G)$$

is then the zero homomorphism and its kernel is the entire group $C_0(K; G)$.

Each 0-chain is a cycle so that we have $Z_0(K; G) = C_0(K; G)$ and consequently $H_0(K; G) = C_0(K; G)/B_0(K; G)$. These conventions will be adopted here and the definitions are repeated for ease of reference.

> DEFINITION 19. For any complex K, the 0-dimensional cycle and homology groups are given by $Z_0(K; G) = C_0(K; G)$ and $H_0(K; G) = C_0(K; G)/B_0(K; G)$.

It may be well to mention in connection with the present discussion that according to formula (8) the boundary of an oriented 1-simplex is given by

$$(9) \qquad \partial\langle a_i, a_j \rangle = a_j - a_i.$$

This formula is employing the dual usage described in Section 6 whereby the same symbol designates an oriented simplex and also the corresponding elementary integral chain. In other words, it is assumed that $s^1 = \Delta(a_i, a_j)$ is a 1-simplex in a complex K and that a definite orientation has been assigned to K. Now the assigned orientation K^α contains either the oriented simplex $\langle a_i, a_j \rangle$ or its negative $\langle a_j, a_i \rangle$. In either case, formula (9) is correct. In the first case, the symbol $\langle a_i, a_j \rangle$ represents an elementary integral 1-chain of K^α and in the second case it represents the negative of an elementary chain. The right hand side of (9) denotes the 0-chain which assigns $+1$ to the vertex a_j and -1 to the vertex a_i.

9. GEOMETRIC INTERPRETATIONS OF CYCLES AND BOUNDARIES

In this section an attempt will be made to add a little intuitive geometric flavor to the rather abstract constructions we have been through thus far. This is solely for the satisfaction of the reader and future developments will make no appeal to the material here.

A convenient method of orienting a complex is to list its entire set of vertices in some arbitrary order. Each simplex is then assigned an orientation by this order restricted to its set of vertices. Let us orient the complexes of Examples 5, 6, and 7 by listing the vertices of each in increasing numerical order of their subscripts as indicated. We shall refer to these oriented complexes as T^2, K, and P^2.

Consider the elementary chain $\langle a_0, a_1, a_3 \rangle$ in T^2. This corresponds to the triangle in the upper left hand corner of the diagram. By (8) we have

$$\partial\langle a_0, a_1, a_3 \rangle = \langle a_1, a_3 \rangle - \langle a_0, a_3 \rangle + \langle a_0, a_1 \rangle .$$

The chain on the right of this last equation could also be written $\langle a_1, a_3 \rangle + \langle a_3, a_0 \rangle + \langle a_0, a_1 \rangle$ and in this form it is seen to correspond to a traversal of the boundary of the triangle $\langle a_0, a_1, a_3 \rangle$ starting at a_1 and going by way of a_3, a_0, and back to a_1. This may give some indication of the origin of the term "boundary" as applied to chains.

Next consider the rectangular region composed of the two triangles in the upper left of the diagram for T^2. We may indicate an orientation of this region by drawing a circular arrow thus:

This orientation of the rectangular region induces an orientation of the two triangles indicated by

This pair of oriented triangles, and consequently the rectangular region, corresponds to the integral 2-chain $\langle a_0, a_1, a_3 \rangle + \langle a_1, a_4, a_3 \rangle$ whose boundary we compute by (8) to be the 1-chain $\langle a_0, a_1 \rangle + \langle a_1, a_4 \rangle + \langle a_4, a_3 \rangle + \langle a_3, a_0 \rangle$. The boundary 1-chain so computed is seen to correspond to the boundary of the oriented rectangular region. Observe that the diagonal $\langle a_1, a_3 \rangle$ appears twice during the computation with different signs and consequently cancels out of the final result.

Now let us look at the integral 1-chain $\langle a_0, a_1 \rangle + \langle a_1, a_2 \rangle + \langle a_2, a_5 \rangle$ of T^2. This chain represents a kind of a path in T^2 from a_0 to a_5

and its boundary is $a_5 - a_0$. In general, the boundary of a 1-chain representing a path like this will be its terminal vertex minus its initial vertex. If these two vertices are the same—that is, if the path is "closed"—then the chain will be a cycle. The original idea of a cycle was a path that starts out, goes around somewhere, and returns to its starting point. If the closed path comprises the boundary of some region, then it is thought of as a bounding cycle. For example, a little closed path on the surface of the torus (such as the cycle $\langle a_1, a_3 \rangle + \langle a_3, a_0 \rangle + \langle a_0, a_1 \rangle$ mentioned earlier) will be a boundary. On the other hand, a longitudinal circle on a torus is the boundary of no region and is thought of as a nonbounding cycle. Examples of nonbounding cycles are afforded by the chains

$$c_1^1 = \langle a_0, a_1 \rangle + \langle a_1, a_2 \rangle + \langle a_2, a_0 \rangle$$

$$c_2^1 = \langle a_3, a_4 \rangle + \langle a_4, a_5 \rangle + \langle a_5, a_3 \rangle$$

of T^2. It is clear that these chains are cycles and it is not too difficult to see that neither is a boundary. The fact that neither c_1^1 nor c_2^1 bounds means that they represent nonzero elements h_1 and h_2 in $H_1(T^2, Z)$. Actually, it turns out that h_1 and h_2 are the same. To see that this is so, one must verify that $c_1^1 - c_2^1$ bounds. The reader is urged to do this by showing that $c_1^1 - c_2^1$ is the boundary of the chain corresponding to the region made up of the six uppermost triangles in the figure for T^2.

Let us now turn to the complex K of Example 6 (the Klein bottle). This time the integral 1-cycle $c^1 = \langle a_0, a_3 \rangle + \langle a_3, a_6 \rangle + \langle a_6, a_0 \rangle$ does not bound but, strangely enough, $2c^1$ does bound. It would be rather laborious but the reader should be able to write a 2-chain whose boundary is $2c^1$. Each of the 18 oriented 2-simplexes would occur in the expression for the required 2-chain with coefficient either $+1$ or -1 and it would be a matter of determining these coefficients.

An important goal in the exposition of homology theory is to work out relationships between the algebraic properties of the homology groups of a complex and the topological or geometric properties of the space of the complex. For example, if $H_1(K; Z) \neq 0$, there exists a non-bounding 1-cycle in K. This means that the closed path in the polytope $|K|$ representing this cycle is not the boundary of a region and this can happen only if the path circles around a "hole" in the space. In general, a nonzero element in the group $H_r(K; Z)$ reveals the presence of an r-dimensional "hole" or "cavity" in the space.

EXERCISE 6

1. In the complex T^2 (Example 5) find a 2-chain whose boundary is the 1-chain $\langle a_0, a_1 \rangle + \langle a_1, a_2 \rangle + \langle a_2, a_4 \rangle + \langle a_4, a_3 \rangle + \langle a_3, a_0 \rangle$.

2. Show that in the complex K (Example 6) the 1-cycles $z_1^1 = \langle a_6, a_7 \rangle + \langle a_7, a_5 \rangle + \langle a_5, a_6 \rangle$ and $z_2^1 = \langle a_6, a_7 \rangle + \langle a_7, a_8 \rangle + \langle a_8, a_6 \rangle$ are homologous.

3. Consider the cycle $z^1 = \langle a_3, a_5 \rangle + \langle a_5, a_4 \rangle + \langle a_4, a_3 \rangle$ in the complex P^2 (Example 7). Show that $2z^1$ is the boundary of the 2-chain $\langle a_0, a_1, a_2 \rangle + \langle a_0, a_2, a_4 \rangle + \langle a_0, a_4, a_3 \rangle + \langle a_0, a_3, a_5 \rangle + \langle a_0, a_5, a_1 \rangle + \langle a_1, a_3, a_2 \rangle + \langle a_1, a_4, a_3 \rangle + \langle a_1, a_5, a_4 \rangle + \langle a_2, a_3, a_5 \rangle + \langle a_2, a_5, a_4 \rangle$.

4. Find a 2-chain in P^2 whose boundary is $2(\langle a_4, a_1 \rangle + \langle a_1, a_2 \rangle + \langle a_2, a_4 \rangle)$.

5. Prove that if c^r is an element of $C_r(K; Z)$ such that $2c^r$ bounds, then c^r is a cycle. Hint: Use the facts that ∂ is a homomorphism, that $\partial\partial(c) = 0$, and that $C_i(K; Z)$ is a free abelian group for each i.

10. CONNECTED COMPLEXES

The 0-dimensional groups are particularly related to the topological property of connectedness. A complex K could be defined to be connected if and only if the point set $|K|$ is connected. However, an equivalent, more workable definition is the following.

DEFINITION 20. A complex K is said to be connected if, for each pair p and q of vertices of K, there exists a sequence $\{a_1^0, s_1^1, a_2^0, s_2^1, \ldots, a_k^0, s_k^1, a_{k+1}^0\}$ where each a_i^0 is a vertex of K; each s_i^1 is a 1-simplex of K; for each $j = 1, 2, \ldots, k$, a_j^0 and a_{j+1}^0 are vertices of s_j^1; and finally, $a_1^0 = p$ and $a_{k+1}^0 = q$.

DEFINITION 21. If K_1 and K_2 are complexes with K_1 contained in K_2, then K_1 is called a subcomplex of K_2. A *component* of a complex is a maximal connected subcomplex.

It is clear from the definition that each connected subcomplex of a complex is contained in a unique component. In particular, each r-simplex of a complex K is an element of a unique component of K.

THEOREM 19. Let v_1^0 and v_2^0 be vertices of a complex K. Then the integral 0-chain $v_2^0 - v_1^0$ bounds if and only if v_1^0 and v_2^0 belong to the same component of K.

Proof: It is clear that v_1^0 and v_2^0 belong to the same component if and only if there exists a sequence $\{a_1^0, s_1^1, \ldots, s_k^1, a_{k+1}^0\}$ (as in Definition 20) with $a_1^0 = v_1^0$ and $a_{k+1}^0 = v_2^0$. Suppose first that such a sequence exists and we orient K in such a way that $\partial s_i^1 = a_{i+1}^0 - a_i^0$ for each $i = 1, 2, \ldots, k$. Now let

$$c^1 = \sum_{i=1}^{k} s_i^1$$

and we have $\partial c^1 = v_2^0 - v_1^0$.

For the converse, the hypothesis is that $v_2^0 - v_1^0$ bounds. It will be shown that v_1^0 and v_2^0 belong to the same component. It is given that $v_2^0 - v_1^0 = \partial(\sum n^i s_i^1)$, and this time orient K in such a way that each integer n^i is nonnegative. This means that we can write

$$v_2^0 - v_1^0 = \partial\left(\sum_{j=1}^{k} s_j^1\right)$$

where there may be repetitions among the $\{s_j^1\}$. For each s_j^1, write $\partial s_j^1 = b_j^0 - a_j^0$. Then $v_2^0 - v_1^0 = \sum b_j^0 - \sum a_j^0$. Thus it is possible to order the $\{s_j^1\}$ in such a way that $a_1^0 = v_1^0$, $b_k^0 = v_2^0$, and $b_{j-1}^0 = a_j^0$ for $j = 2, \ldots, k$. This is, however, a sequence from v_1^0 to v_2^0 as given in Definition 20, and the proof is complete.

Further progress in the discussion of the 0-dimensional homology groups depends on the concept of the Kronecker index of a 0-dimensional chain.

DEFINITION 22. Let $c^0 = \sum g^i a_i^0$ be a 0-chain of a complex K over G. The *Kronecker index* of c^0, denoted by $\text{In}(c^0)$, is defined to be the group element $\sum g^i$.

THEOREM 20. (a) If c_1^0 and c_2^0 are elements of $C_0(K; G)$, then $\text{In}(c_1^0 + c_2^0) = \text{In}(c_1^0) + \text{In}(c_2^0)$.

(b) If $c^0 \in B_0(K; G)$, then $\text{In}(c^0) = 0$.

(c) If K is connected and $\text{In}(c^0) = 0$, then $c^0 \in B_0(K; G)$.

Proof of (b): If $s^1 = \langle a_0, a_1 \rangle$ is an oriented 1-simplex of K, then $\text{In}(\partial s^1) = \text{In}(a_1 - a_0) = 0$. Consequently, if $c^1 = \sum g^i s_i^1$, then $\text{In}(\partial c^1) = \sum g^i \text{In}(\partial s_i^1) = 0$.

Proof of (c): Suppose that K is connected and let $a_0, a_1, \ldots, a_k$ be the vertices of K. For each $i = 1, 2, \ldots, k$ there exists a 1-chain s_i^1 such that $\partial(s_i^1) = a_i - a_0$. Now let $c^0 = \sum_{i=0}^{k} g^i a_i$ be an element of $C_0(K; G)$ and suppose that $\text{In}(c^0) = 0$. This means that $g^0 = -(\sum_{i=1}^{k} g^i)$ so that

$$c^0 = \sum_{i=0}^{k} g^i a_i = g^0 a_0 + \sum_{i=1}^{k} g^i a_i = \sum_{i=1}^{k} g^i(a_i - a_0) = \sum_{i=1}^{k} g^i \, \partial(s_i^1) = \partial\left(\sum_{i=1}^{k} g^i s_i^1\right).$$

THEOREM 21. If K is a connected complex, then $H_0(K; G)$ is isomorphic to G.

Proof: The homomorphism

$$\text{In} : C_0(K; G) \to G$$

is surjective with kernel $B_0(K; G)$. Hence the quotient group $C_0(K; G)/B_0(K; G) = H_0(K; G)$ is isomorphic to G.

11. THE REDUCED ZERO-DIMENSIONAL GROUPS

It has already been pointed out that the approach to the construction of the 0-dimensional homology groups adopted in Section 8 was the simplest possible. The agreement there was to define the group of 0-cycles to be the entire group $C_0(K; G)$. This definition is consistent with the convention that a complex K contains no simplexes of dimension -1 and consequently $C_{-1}(K; G) = 0$.

An alternative definition of $Z_0(K; G)$ is suggested by Theorem 20. The idea is to *augment* the complex K by adjoining to it the unique (-1)-dimensional simplex which is the null set. In other words, the augmented complex is the set $K_a = K \cup \{\varnothing\}$. It is customary to omit the subscript a and to use the same symbol K for the augmented complex.

Now, since the augmented complex contains a single simplex of dimension -1, it follows that $C_{-1}(K; G)$ is isomorphic to G and it will cause no confusion to consider this isomorphism as an identification. That is to say, we define $C_{-1}(K; G) = G$. The boundary operator $\partial : C_0(K; G) \to G$ is then defined to be the homomorphism In of Theorem 20.

According to this definition, the group of 0-cycles is the kernel of the homomorphism In, and by Theorem 20 $B_0(K; G)$ is contained in Kernel(In). We then have the following definition.

DEFINITION 23. The *reduced* 0-dimensional homology group of a complex K with coefficients in G is the quotient group $\tilde{H}_0(K; G) = \text{Kernel(In)}/B_0(K; G)$.

The next proposition is an easy consequence of Theorem 19.

THEOREM 22. A complex K is connected if and only if $\tilde{H}_0(K; Z) = 0$.

EXERCISE 7

1. A subset X of R^n is said to be *convex* provided the line segment (a, b) is contained in X for each pair of distinct points a, b in X. Show that each convex subset of R^n is connected.

2. Prove that a simplex is convex and hence connected.

3. Prove that a complex K is connected if and only if the point set $|K|$ is connected.

4. A complex K is connected if and only if it is not the union of two disjoint subcomplexes.

5. If $K_1, K_2, \ldots, K_m$ are the components of a complex K, then $H_0(K; G)$ is isomorphic to the direct sum $G \oplus \cdots \oplus G$ for m summands. Hint: In each component K_i, select a vertex v_i and show that each element of $C_0(K; G)$ is homologous to a unique chain of the form $\sum_{i=1}^m g^i v_i$.

6. If $K_1, K_2, \ldots, K_m$ are the components of a complex K, then $\tilde{H}_0(K; G)$ is isomorphic to the direct sum $G \oplus \cdots \oplus G$ for $m - 1$ summands.

7. Let K be a complex consisting of a single vertex. Describe $Z_0(K; G)$ and $B_0(K; G)$. Prove directly that $H_0(K; G)$ is isomorphic to G.

12. SIMPLICIAL MAPS AND
INDUCED HOMOMORPHISMS

In the theory of simplicial complexes, the concept of a *simplicial map* is associated with the complexes which are the basic units. Just as a group homomorphism is a mapping of groups which is compatible with the algebraic structure, a simplicial map is a mapping of complexes related in a natural way to the simplicial structure of the complexes.

For the purpose of the next definition, recall that the symbol K^0 is used to denote the set of vertices of a complex K. A mapping $\tau : K^0 \to L^0$ is said to be *simplex preserving* if for each simplex $\Delta(a_0, a_1, \ldots, a_r)$ of K, the set $\{\tau(a_0), \tau(a_1), \ldots, \tau(a_r)\}$ is the set of vertices, not necessarily distinct, of a simplex of L.

DEFINITION 24. A simplex preserving function

$$\tau : K^0 \to L^0$$

is also called a simplicial map from K to L, and we write

$$\tau : K \to L.$$

The idea now is to work out a method of assigning a group homomorphism

$$h : C_r(K; G) \to C_r(L; G)$$

to each simplicial map $\tau : K \to L$. Actually, there will be a family of homomorphisms assigned to each simplicial map, one for each nonnegative integer r and one for each coefficient group G. In the applications, however, the integer r and the group G are usually considered fixed and the homomorphism h is thought of as primarily a function of the mapping τ. For this reason, we shall at present omit from the notation any reference to r and G and indicate the homomorphism assigned to the map τ by the symbol $\tau_\#$. Also, $\tau_\#$ is called the homomorphism induced by τ.

For purposes of the next definition we say that a simplicial map $\tau : K \to L$ collapses a simplex $\Delta(a_0, a_1, \ldots, a_r)$ of K if there exists a pair of distinct vertices a_i and a_j such that $\tau(a_i) = \tau(a_j)$. This happens if and only if $\{\tau(a_0), \ldots, \tau(a_r)\}$ are the vertices of a simplex in L of dimension less than r.

DEFINITION 25. Let $\tau : K \to L$ be a simplicial map. Each oriented simplex $s^r \in K$ is an elementary integral r-chain of K and the symbol $\tau_\#(s^r)$ denotes the integral r-chain of L given by

$$\tau_\#(s^r) = \begin{cases} 0 & \text{if } \tau \text{ collapses } s^r, \\ \tau(s^r) & \text{otherwise.} \end{cases}$$

THEOREM 23. Let $\tau : K \to L$ be a simplicial map. For each nonnegative integer r and for each coefficient group G there exists a unique homomorphism

$$h : C_r(K; G) \to C_r(L; G)$$

such that if $c = \sum g^i s_i^r$ is an element of $C_r(K; G)$, then

$$h(c) = h(\sum g^i s_i^r) = \sum g^i \tau_\#(s_i^r).$$

The homomorphism h is denoted by the symbol $\tau_\#$.

The proof of Theorem 23 is left as an exercise.

For each simplicial map $\tau : K \to L$ and for each coefficient group G we have the following diagram of groups and homomorphisms.

$$\cdots \to C_{r+1}(K; G) \xrightarrow{\partial} C_r(K; G) \xrightarrow{\partial} C_{r-1}(K; G) \xrightarrow{\partial} \cdots$$
$$\tau_\# \downarrow \qquad \tau_\# \downarrow \qquad \tau_\# \downarrow$$
$$\cdots \to C_{r+1}(L; G) \xrightarrow{\partial} C_r(L; G) \xrightarrow{\partial} C_{r-1}(L; G) \xrightarrow{\partial} \cdots$$

An important property of these induced homomorphisms is that of "commuting" with the boundary operator. The statement of this property is the content of Theorem 24 which can be paraphrased by saying that each square of the diagram above is commutative.

THEOREM 24. For each element c of $C_r(K; G)$,

$$\partial \tau_\#(c) = \tau_\# \partial(c).$$

It will be sufficient to prove that for each oriented r-simplex $s^r = \langle a_0, a_1, \ldots, a_r \rangle$ of K, $\partial \tau_\#(s^r) = \tau_\# \partial(s^r)$. There are two cases.

CASE 1: τ does not collapse s^r. We have

$$\partial \tau_\# (s^r) = \partial < \tau(a_0),\, \tau(a_1),\, \ldots,\, \tau(a_r) >$$
$$= \sum (-1)^i < \tau(a_0),\, \ldots,\, \tau(\hat{a}_i),\, \ldots,\, \tau(a_r) >$$
$$= \tau_\# (\sum (-1)^i < a_0,\, \ldots,\, \hat{a}_i,\, \ldots,\, a_r >)$$
$$= \tau_\# \, \partial(s^r).$$

CASE 2: τ collapses s^r. In this case we may suppose that s^r is oriented so that $\tau(a_0) = \tau(a_1)$. Then

$$\tau_\# \, \partial(s^r) = \tau_\# (\sum (-1)^i \langle a_0,\, \ldots,\, \hat{a}_i,\, \ldots,\, a_r \rangle)$$
$$= \tau_\# \langle a_1, a_2,\, \ldots,\, a_r \rangle - \tau_\# \langle a_0, a_2,\, \ldots,\, a_r \rangle$$
$$+ \sum_{i=2}^{r} (-1)^i \tau_\# \langle a_0,\, \ldots,\, \hat{a}_i,\, \ldots,\, a_r \rangle = 0.$$

Also, $\partial \tau_\# (s^r) = \partial(0) = 0$, and the proof is complete.

EXERCISE 8

1. Let $\tau : K \rightarrow L$ be a simplicial map. Use Theorem 24 to prove that $\tau_\# : C_r(K;\, G) \rightarrow C_r(L;\, G)$ maps $Z_r(K;\, G)$ into $Z_r(L;\, G)$ and $B_r(K;\, G)$ into $B_r(L;\, G)$.

2. Show that a constant map $K^0 \rightarrow L^0$ is a simplicial map.

3. Refer to the diagram for Example 5. Show that a simplicial map $\phi : T^2 \rightarrow T^2$ is determined by mapping each vertex onto the one just below it in the diagram.

4. Show that a counterclockwise notation through 120 degrees of the figure for Example 7 provides a simplicial map $\psi : P^2 \rightarrow P^2$.

5. Show that the composite of two simplicial maps is a simplicial map.

CHAPTER II

THE HOMOLOGY GROUPS
OF A POLYTOPE

In Chapter I we defined for each complex K the homology groups $H_r(K; G)$. As explained earlier, the group $H_r(K; G)$ depends on the integer r and the coefficient group G. In spite of this, it is frequently convenient to think of r and G as being fixed so that the homology group becomes a function of the complex K alone.

A second construction covered in Chapter I assigned to each complex K a polytope $|K|$. A crucial result of the present chapter will be that if complexes K and L are triangulations of the same polytope X, then the groups $H_r(K; G)$ and $H_r(L; G)$ are isomorphic. More specifically, under these circumstances we shall be able to establish the existence of a definite isomorphism of the homology groups. This will enable us to define a homology group $H_r(X; G)$ which will be isomorphic to $H_r(K; G)$ for every triangulation K of X. Precisely because this new group is independent of any triangulation it can properly be called a function of the polytope X.

Also in this chapter, we shall work out a process which assigns to each polytope map $f: X \to Y$ an "induced" homomorphism $f_* : H_r (X; G) \to H_r(Y; G)$. We shall see that if a map f is a homeomorphism, then the induced homomorphism f_* is an isomorphism. Thus the homology group $H_r(X, G)$ is a topological invariant of the polytope X.

The topological invariance of the homology groups will be the key to applications presented in Chapter III. On the one hand, for each polytope map $f: X \to Y$, properties of the induced homomorphism $f_* : H_r (X; G) \to H_r(Y, G)$ can be deduced from the topological invariance. On the other hand, these groups and homomorphisms can be computed from any convenient triangulations of X and Y. An interplay between these two approaches will lead to proofs of geometric results, including generalizations of the theorems in the Introduction.

As a background for the developments of this chapter, it will be helpful to consider a unifying setting for a variety of mathematical systems. For an example of the sort of thing envisioned here one observes that in group theory a study is made of certain objects called groups and certain mappings called homomorphisms, while in topology the objects under study are topological spaces and the mappings are continuous functions. A third example is afforded by the theory of simplicial complexes. Here complexes are the objects and the mappings are simplicial maps. In each of these examples a particular class of objects is under study and, equally important, in each case an integral part of the mathematical system is a class of mappings associated with the objects in the system. There is a concept called "category" whose definition is motivated by elements of similarity in systems like the three mentioned above.

In the next few paragraphs time will be taken for the purpose of presenting two algebraic results which will be useful in the near future. Usually no explicit reference will be given when these theorems are used.

THEOREM 1. Let $G_1 \xrightarrow{h_1} G_2 \xrightarrow{h_2} G_1$ be a diagram of abelian groups and homomorphisms. Suppose also that the composed homomorphism $h_2 h_1$ is the identity mapping of G_1. Then the group G_2 is the direct sum of the image of h_1 and the kernel of h_2.

Proof: First let x be an element of $\operatorname{Im}(h_1) \cap \operatorname{Ker}(h_2)$. Then $x = h_1(y)$ and $0 = h_2(x) = h_2 h_1(y) = y$ implies that $x = 0$. Also, for any element x of G_2 we have $x = \{x - h_1 h_2(x)\} + h_1 h_2(x)$. Now $x - h_1 h_2(x)$ is an element of $\operatorname{Ker}(h_2)$ and $h_1 h_2(x)$ is an element of $\operatorname{Im}(h_1)$, and this completes the proof.

THEOREM 2. (The induced homomorphism theorem.) Let A, B, C, and D be abelian groups and let α, β, and γ be homomorphisms as shown.

$$
\begin{array}{ccc}
A & \overset{\bar{\gamma}}{\dashrightarrow} & D \\
\alpha \uparrow & & \uparrow \beta \\
B & \overset{\gamma}{\longrightarrow} & C
\end{array}
$$

Furthermore, suppose that α is surjective and that γ maps the kernel of α into the kernel of β. Then there exists a unique homomorphism $\bar{\gamma} : A \to D$ such that $\bar{\gamma}\alpha = \beta\gamma$.

The proof of Theorem 2 will be left as an exercise.

1. CATEGORIES

The mathematical systems mentioned in the preceding paragraphs are all special cases of the next definition.

DEFINITION 1. A *category* consists of two classes; first, a class of objects, and second, a class of morphisms satisfying the following axioms.

(1) For each ordered pair (X, Y) of objects there is a set $\operatorname{Hom}(X, Y)$ of morphisms.

(2) If (X, Y) and (U, V) are distinct ordered pairs of objects, then $\operatorname{Hom}(X, Y)$ and $\operatorname{Hom}(U, V)$ are disjoint.

(3) For each ordered triple (X, Y, Z) of objects and for each pair of morphisms $f \in \operatorname{Hom}(X, Y)$ and $g \in \operatorname{Hom}(Y, Z)$, there is a composite morphism $gf \in \operatorname{Hom}(X, Z)$.

(4) If $f \in \text{Hom}(X, Y)$, $g \in \text{Hom}(Y, Z)$, and $h \in \text{Hom}(Z, W)$, then $h(gf) = (hg)f$.

(5) For each object X there is a morphism $I_X \in \text{Hom}(X, X)$ such that for each morphism $f \in \text{Hom}(X, Y)$, $I_Y f = f = f I_X$.

For purposes of reference, we again list the three categories described earlier.

EXAMPLE 1: The category of groups and homomorphisms.

EXAMPLE 2: The category of topological spaces and continuous maps.

EXAMPLE 3: The category of simplicial complexes and simplicial maps.

In each of these examples the category is described by mentioning first the class of objects and then the class of morphisms. Also, in each of these examples a morphism $f \in \text{Hom}(X, Y)$ is a particular kind of function from X to Y. It is true that in many categories the morphisms are functions and for this reason the language and notation of functions are used for morphisms in general. As an example, for $f \in \text{Hom}(X, Y)$, we write $f: X \to Y$ or $X \xrightarrow{f} Y$. Objects X and Y are called the domain and range of each morphism $f \in \text{Hom}(X, Y)$. Again, the morphism I_X is called the identity morphism of X. If $f: X \to Y$ and $g: Y \to X$ are morphisms and $gf = I_X$, then g is called a left inverse of f and f is called a right inverse of g. The proofs of many elementary propositions concerning functions generalize immediately for morphisms. In particular, if a morphism f has a left and a right inverse, then these two are identical and in this case f is called an *equivalence*.

In constructing proofs one frequently works with *diagrams* of objects and morphisms. Examples are now given.

It is often important to know that a diagram of objects and morphisms is *commutative*. The triangular diagram above is said to be commutative if f is the composition of g and h, that is if $f = hg$. The square diagram is commutative provided $kf = hg$.

In general, script letters such as $\mathcal{K}$ or $\mathcal{L}$ will be used to denote categories. Some such notation is necessary when distinct categories having the same class of objects are under consideration. If X and Y are objects of categories $\mathcal{K}$ and $\mathcal{L}$, then $\mathrm{Hom}_{\mathcal{K}}(X, Y)$ and $\mathrm{Hom}_{\mathcal{L}}(X, Y)$ designate the corresponding sets of morphisms.

DEFINITION 2. A category $\mathcal{L}$ is a subcategory of a category $\mathcal{K}$ provided the following hold true.

(1) Each object of $\mathcal{L}$ is an object of $\mathcal{K}$.

(2) For each ordered pair of objects (X, Y) in $\mathcal{L}$, $\mathrm{Hom}_{\mathcal{L}}(X, Y)$ is contained in $\mathrm{Hom}_{\mathcal{K}}(X, Y)$.

(3) For morphisms $f \in \mathrm{Hom}_{\mathcal{L}}(X, Y)$ and $g \in \mathrm{Hom}_{\mathcal{L}}(Y, Z)$, the composition gf is the same morphism in $\mathrm{Hom}_{\mathcal{L}}(X, Z)$ and $\mathrm{Hom}_{\mathcal{K}}(X, Z)$.

Next we have some further examples of categories that will be of importance in our work.

EXAMPLE 4: The category $\mathcal{T}$ of topological pairs and continuous functions. A topological pair (X, A) is a topological space X and a subset A. The objects here are topological pairs and the morphisms are continuous functions from X to Y which map A into B. For such a function f, we write $f : (X, A) \to (Y, B)$.

EXAMPLE 5: The cageory $\mathcal{S}$ of simplicial pairs and simplicial maps. A simplicial pair (K, L) is an ordered pair consisting of a complex K and a subcomplex L. A morphism in this category is a simplicial map

$$\tau : (K_1, L_1) \to (K_2, L_2)$$

from K_1 to K_2 which maps L_1 into L_2.

EXAMPLE 6: The category $\mathscr{C}$ of *chain complexes*. A chain complex is a sequence of abelian groups and homomorphisms

$$\cdots \xrightarrow{\partial_{q+2}} C_{q+1} \xrightarrow{\partial_{q+1}} C_q \xrightarrow{\partial_q} C_{q-1} \xrightarrow{\partial_{q-1}} \cdots$$

satisfying the condition

$$\partial_i \partial_{i+1} = 0 \qquad \text{for each } i.$$

A single upper case letter is used to indicate a chain complex; for example, $C = \{C_q, \partial_q\}$. Observe that the homomorphism ∂_q lowers the index by one; that is, ∂_q is from C_q to C_{q-1}.

In the category $\mathscr{C}$, the objects are chain complexes and the morphisms are *chain transformations*. A chain transformation from a chain complex $C = \{C_q, \partial_q\}$ to a chain complex $C' = \{C'_q, \partial'_q\}$ is a sequence of homomorphisms $\tau_q : C_q \to C'_q$ such that for each q, $\tau_{q-1}\partial_q = \partial'_q \tau_q$. Thus each chain transformation is a "commutative ladder":

$$\cdots \xrightarrow{\partial_{q+2}} C_{q+1} \xrightarrow{\partial_{q+1}} C_q \xrightarrow{\partial_q} C_{q-1} \xrightarrow{\partial_{q-1}} \cdots$$
$$\downarrow{\tau_{q+1}} \qquad \downarrow{\tau_q} \qquad \downarrow{\tau_{q-1}}$$
$$\cdots \xrightarrow{\partial'_{q+2}} C'_{q+1} \xrightarrow{\partial'_{q+1}} C'_q \xrightarrow{\partial'_q} C'_{q-1} \xrightarrow{\partial'_{q-1}} \cdots$$

The sequence of homomorphisms making up a chain transformation is indicated by a single letter; $\tau = \{\tau_q\}$ and we write $\tau : C \to C'$. This is equivalent to $\tau \in \text{Hom}_{\mathscr{C}}(C, C')$.

A chain complex is a sequence indexed by the entire set of integers. That is, for each integer r—positive, zero, or negative—we have a homomorphism $\partial_r : C_r \to C_{r-1}$. In Chapter I we saw that for each complex K and for each coefficient group G, the sequence made up of the boundary homomorphisms $\partial : C_{q+1}(K; G) \to C_q(K; G)$ is a chain complex. The chain complex $C(K; G) = \{C_q(K; G), \partial_q\}$ is said to be *nonnegative* since we have, according to definition, $C_q(K; G) = 0$ for $q < 0$. The nonnegative chain complexes are the objects in a subcategory of the category of chain complexes.

EXAMPLE 7: The category $\mathscr{H}$ of *graded groups*. A graded group $G = \{G_q\}$ is a sequence of groups indexed by the set of integers. The family of homology groups $\{H_q(K; G)\}$ associated with a complex K is a graded group provided we set $H_q(K; G) = 0$ for $q < 0$. In this category a morphism from a graded group G to a graded group H is a sequence of homomorphisms $\{\alpha_q : G_q \to H_q\}$. For such a sequence we write $\alpha = \{\alpha_q\}$ and $\alpha : G \to H$.

EXERCISE 1

1. Prove Theorem 2.

2. A category $\mathcal{K}$ is defined as follows: The objects are positive integers. For objects a and b, the set $\mathrm{Hom}_{\mathcal{K}}(a, b)$ is defined to consist of all ordered triples (b, x, a) where x is a common divisor of a and b. Composition of morphisms is defined by $(c, y, b)(b, x, a) = (c, (x,y), a)$ where (x, y) is the highest common divisor of x and y. Verify the axioms for a category.

3. Which morphisms of the category $\mathcal{K}$ (Problem 2) have left inverses? Which are equivalences?

4. Show that there is a category of groups and surjective (injective) homomorphisms.

5. Verify that in the category of chain complexes the chain transformations satisfy the axioms for morphisms.

2. FUNCTORS

Suppose now that one wishes to consider a category whose objects are categories. An immediate question concerns the nature of the morphisms. Let us assume for the moment that such a category exists and call the morphisms *functors*. It seems reasonable to require that a functor map the objects of one category into the objects of another and it is also clear that a functor must do something about the morphisms of the two categories. While it is not the purpose here to consider the logical difficulties involved in the notion of the "category of all categories," we can admit that the idea of a functor is useful and formulate a precise definition. Since there is a choice to be made regarding the way in which a functor handles the morphisms, this leads to the definitions of two kinds of functors.

DEFINITION 3. A *covariant* functor T from a category $\mathcal{K}$ to a category $\mathcal{L}$ is a pair of functions (both denoted by the letter T). First, the *object function* maps the objects of $\mathcal{K}$ into the objects of $\mathscr{L}$, and second, the *morphism function* maps the morphisms of $\mathscr{K}$ into the morphisms of $\mathscr{L}$ satisfying these conditions.

(1) If $f \in \mathrm{Hom}_{\mathscr{K}}(X, Y)$, then $T(f) \in \mathrm{Hom}_{\mathscr{L}}(T(X,)\underline{T(Y)})$.

(2) If $f \in \mathrm{Hom}_{\mathscr{K}}(X, Y)$ and $g \in \mathrm{Hom}_{\mathscr{K}}(Y, Z)$, then $T(gf) = \underline{T(g)T(f)}$.

(3) For each object X of $\mathscr{K}$, $T(I_X) = I_{T(X)}$.

The functor T is said to be *contravariant* provided the following version of conditions (1) and (2) are satisfied.

(1′) If $f \in \mathrm{Hom}_{\mathscr{K}}(X, Y)$, then $T(f) \in \mathrm{Hom}_{\mathscr{L}}(\underline{T(Y)}, T(X))$.

(2′) If $f \in \mathrm{Hom}_{\mathscr{K}}(X, Y)$ and $g \in \mathrm{Hom}_{\mathscr{L}}(Y, Z)$, then $T(gf) = \underline{T(f)T(g)}$.

In our applications all functors will be of the covariant variety. Contravariant functors are important in other situations.

EXAMPLE 8: A chain complex is a graded group with additional structure, and a chain transformation is a morphism of graded groups with the property of commuting with the "boundary" homomorphisms of the chain complex. Consequently there is a covariant functor which assigns to each chain complex $\{C_q, \partial_q\}$ the graded group $\{C_q\}$ obtained by neglecting the homomorphisms $\{\partial_q\}$ and which is the identity mapping on the class of chain transformations. This is an example of a *forgetful* functor which merely neglects certain structure in a category.

EXAMPLE 9: Consider the category whose objects are groups and whose morphisms are surjective homomorphisms. There is a covariant functor T from this category to the category of abelian groups which assigns to each group G its center $T(G)$. If f is an element of $\mathrm{Hom}(G, H)$, then $T(f) = f \,|\, T(G)$.

The present chapter is devoted largely to the study of several important functors. To describe the first of these we need the notion of a linear function $f : |s^r| \to |s^t|$ where s^r and s^t are simplexes; the idea is that a linear function f maps each segment $\langle p, q \rangle$ linearly onto the segment $\langle f(p), f(q) \rangle$ for $p, q \in |s^r|$. This is equivalent to the following definition.

DEFINITION 4. A function $f: |s^r| \to |s^t|$ is said to be linear provided whenever $p_0, p_1, \ldots, p_k$ are elements of $|s^r|$ and $\lambda^0, \lambda^1, \ldots, \lambda^k$ are nonnegative real numbers such that $\sum \lambda^i = 1$, then $f(\sum \lambda^i p_i) = \sum \lambda^i f(p_i)$.

Notice that a linear mapping f is determined by its values on the vertices $\{a_i\}$ of s^r since each point p of $|s^r|$ can be written $p = \sum \lambda^i a_i$, and consequently

(1) $$f(p) = \sum \lambda^i f(a_i).$$

Conversely, if the mapping f is originally given only on the vertices, then formula (1) determines a unique linear extension of f. In particular, if $\tau : s^r \to s^t$ is a simplicial map, there exists a unique linear function $f: |s^r| \to |s^t|$ such that $f(a_i) = \tau(a_i)$ for each a_i. The continuity of the extension is a consequence of the continuity of barycentric coordinates.

DEFINITION 5. The symbol $|\ |$ will be used to denote the covariant functor from the category of simplicial pairs to the category of topological pairs which assigns to each simplicial pair (K, L) the topological pair $(|K|, |L|)$ and which assigns to each simplicial map $\tau : (K_1, L_1) \to (K_2, L_2)$ the continuous function

$$|\tau| : (|K_1|, |L_1|) \to (|K_2|, |L_2|),$$

which is the unique linear extension of τ on the space of each simplex of K_1.

To justify this definition one must show first, if $\tau : (K, L) \to (K, L)$ is the identity, then $|\tau|$ is the identity and second, if $\tau : (K_1, L_1) \to (K_2, L_2)$ and $\sigma : (K_2, L_2) \to (K_3, L_3)$, then $|\sigma\tau| = |\sigma|\,|\tau|$. The reader will be asked to do this in an exercise.

Before the definition of the next functor can be given, we need to examine the notion of a quotient chain complex. First we have the definition of a chain subcomplex.

DEFINITION 6. Let $G = \{G_q, \partial_q\}$ and $H = \{H_q, \partial'_q\}$ be chain complexes. Then H is a chain subcomplex of G if, for each q, H_q is a subgroup of G_q and $\partial'_q = \partial_q | H_q$.

Suppose now that H is a chain subcomplex of G, and for each q let $\Theta_q : G_q \to G_q/H_q$ be the natural homomorphism. Then for each q we have the following commutative diagram.

$$
\begin{array}{ccccc}
G_{q+1}/H_{q+1} & \xrightarrow{\bar{\partial}_{q+1}} & G_q/H_q & \xrightarrow{\bar{\partial}_q} & G_{q-1}/H_{q-1} \\
\Big\uparrow{\scriptstyle\Theta_{q+1}} & & \Big\uparrow{\scriptstyle\Theta_q} & & \Big\uparrow{\scriptstyle\Theta_{q-1}} \\
G_{q+1} & \xrightarrow{\partial_{q+1}} & G_q & \xrightarrow{\partial_q} & G_{q-1}
\end{array}
$$

The homomorphism $\bar{\partial}_q$ is the homomorphism induced by ∂_q and it is clear that $\bar{\partial}_q\bar{\partial}_{q+1} = 0$ so that $\{G_q/H_q, \bar{\partial}_q\}$ is a chain complex.

DEFINITION 7. Let $H = \{H_q, \partial'_q\}$ be a chain subcomplex of the chain complex $G = \{G_q, \partial_q\}$. The quotient chain complex G/H is defined by $G/H = \{G_q/H_q, \bar{\partial}_q\}$.

EXAMPLE 10: If K is a simplicial complex, the symbol $C(K; G)$ will be used to represent the chain complex

$$\to C_{q+1}(K; G) \xrightarrow{\partial_{q+1}} C_q(K; G) \xrightarrow{\partial_q} C_{q-1}(K; G) \to$$

where $C_q(K; G)$ and ∂_q are the chain groups and boundary homomorphisms defined in Chapter I.

For each simplicial pair (K, L) there is a natural injection $C(L; G) \to C(K; G)$ which is taken as an identification so that $C(L; G)$ becomes a chain subcomplex of $C(K; G)$. The symbol $C(K, L; G)$ will be used to represent the quotient chain complex $C(K; G)/C(L; G)$. We wish to establish the existence of a functor whose object function assigns this chain complex to the simplicial pair (K, L). To describe the morphism function we remark that corresponding to each simplicial map

$$\tau : (K_1, L_1) \to (K_2, L_2)$$

there is, for each q, a unique homomorphism $C_q(\tau)$ which makes the following diagram commutative.

$$
\begin{array}{ccc}
C_q(K_1, L_1; G) & \xrightarrow{C_q(\tau)} & C_q(K_2, L_2; G) \\
\Big\uparrow{\scriptstyle\Theta_q} & & \Big\uparrow{\scriptstyle\Phi_q} \\
C_q(K_1; G) & \xrightarrow{\tau_\#} & C_q(K_2; G)
\end{array}
$$

In this diagram Θ_q and Φ_q are natural homomorphisms and $\tau_\#$ is the induced homomorphism defined in Section 12 of Chapter I. The existence and uniqueness of the homomorphism $C_q(\tau)$ follow from Theorem 2.

THEOREM 3. There is for each coefficient group G a covariant functor C from the category of simplicial pairs to the category of chain complexes which assigns to each simplicial pair (K, L) the chain complex $C(K, L; G)$ and to each simplicial map

$$\tau : (K_1, L_1) \to (K_2, L_2)$$

the chain transformation $C(\tau) = \{C_q(\tau)\}$.

Proof: There are two parts to the proof. First, one must show that the collection $C(\tau) = \{C_q(\tau)\}$ is indeed a chain transformation—that is, that the following diagram is commutative.

$$
\begin{array}{ccc}
C_{q+1}(K_1, L_1; G) & \xrightarrow{\bar{\partial}_{q+1}} & C_q(K_1, L_1; G) \\
{\scriptstyle C_{q+1}(\tau)}\downarrow & & \downarrow{\scriptstyle C_q(\tau)} \\
C_{q+1}(K_2, L_2; G) & \xrightarrow{\bar{\partial}_{q+1}} & C_q(K_2, L_2; G)
\end{array}
$$

The proof can best be made by imbedding this diagram in a larger diagram.

What we must do here is prove that the inner square of this diagram is commutative. The outer square of the diagram is commutative by Theorem 24 of Chapter I. The four "trapezoids" of the diagram are commutative because of the definitions of $\bar{\partial}$ and $C(\tau)$.

To begin the proof, consider an element c of $C_{q+1}(K_1, L_1; G)$. Since Θ_{q+1} is surjective, there is an element c' of $C_{q+1}(K_1; G)$ such that $\Theta_{q+1}(c') = c$ and we have

$$C_q(\tau)\bar{\partial}_{q+1}(c) = C_q(\tau)\bar{\partial}_{q+1}\Theta_{q+1}(c') =$$
$$C_q(\tau)\Theta_q \partial_{q+1}(c') = \Phi_q \tau_{\#} \partial_{q+1}(c') =$$
$$\Phi_q \partial_{q+1} \tau_{\#}(c') = \bar{\partial}_{q+1}\Phi_{q+1}\tau_{\#}(c') =$$
$$\bar{\partial}_{q+1}C_{q+1}(\tau)\Theta_{q+1}(c') = \bar{\partial}_{q+1}C_{q+1}(\tau)(c).$$

This completes the first part of the theorem. The type of argument just given by "diagram chasing" is usually omitted after the first example.

To complete the proof of Theorem 3 we must show that if $\tau : (K_1, L_1) \to (K_2, L_2)$ and $\sigma : (K_2, L_2) \to (K_3, L_3)$ are simplicial maps, then $C(\sigma\tau) = C(\sigma)C(\tau)$ and that if $\tau : (K, L) \to (K, L)$ is the identity map, then $C(\tau)$ is the identity map. These propositions follow easily from the results of Chapter I.

In order to lay the groundwork for our next functor, several definitions will be made which are generalizations of developments in Chapter I.

DEFINITION 8. For each chain complex $C = \{C_q, \partial_q\}$ the groups $Z_q(C)$ and $B_q(C)$ are defined by

$$Z_q(C) = \text{Kernel of } \partial_q,$$
$$B_q(C) = \text{Image of } \partial_{q+1}.$$

THEOREM 4. Let C be a chain complex. Then for each q, $B_q(C)$ is contained in $Z_q(C)$.

DEFINITION 9. Let C be a chain complex. The qth homology group of C is the group $H_q(C) = Z_q(C)/B_q(C)$. The graded homology group of C is the graded group $H(C) = \{H_q(C)\}$.

Definition 9 will describe the object function of a functor from the category of chain complexes to the category of graded groups which assigns to each chain complex C the graded homology group $H(C)$. The next step is to associate with each chain transformation $\alpha : C \to C'$ a morphism of graded groups indicated by $H(\alpha) : H(C) \to H(C')$. Let $\alpha = \{\alpha_q\}$ and then for each q, α_q maps $Z_q(C)$ into $Z_q(C')$ and $B_q(C)$ into $B_q(C')$. Hence α_q induces a homomorphism

$$(\alpha_*)_q : H_q(C) \to H_q(C').$$

The morphism $H(\alpha)$ is now defined by $H(\alpha) = \{(\alpha_*)_q\}$.

THEOREM 5. There is a covariant functor H from the category of chain complexes to the category of graded groups which assigns to each chain complex C the graded homology group $H(C)$ and to each chain transformation $\alpha : C \to C'$ the homomorphism $H(\alpha)$.

Proof: It must be shown that for chain transformations $\alpha : C \to C'$ and $\beta : C' \to C''$ we have $((\beta\alpha)_*)_q = (\beta_*)_q(\alpha_*)_q$. This follows directly from the uniqueness part of Theorem 2.

It should be remarked here that a morphism in the category of graded groups is sometimes called a homomorphism of degree zero. The reason for this is that if $G = \{G_q\}$ and $H = \{H_q\}$ are graded groups, then a homomorphism of degree r (written $h : G \to H$) from G to H is a collection of homomorphisms $h = \{h_q : G_q \to H_{q+r}\}$. A chain complex C is a graded group and the boundary operator $\partial : C \to C$ is a homomorphism of degree -1. In the future we shall have occasion to consider homomorphisms of degree $+1$.

In this section we have considered categories $\mathscr{S}, \mathscr{C}, \mathscr{H}$, and $\mathscr{T}$. The objects in these categories are simplicial pairs, chain complexes, graded groups, and topological pairs. We have defined functors as indicated.

$$C : \mathscr{S} \to \mathscr{C}$$
$$H : \mathscr{C} \to \mathscr{H}$$
$$|\,| : \mathscr{S} \to \mathscr{T}$$

We may now consider the composite functor HC from $\mathscr{S}$ to $\mathscr{H}$. This functor assigns to each simplicial pair (K, L) the graded group $HC(K, L) = \{H_q(C(K, L; G))\}$. The notation $H_q(C(K, L; G))$ is always abbreviated $H_q(K, L; G)$ and this group is called the q-dimensional relative homology group of the pair (K, L) with coefficients in G. The composite functor HC assigns to each simplicial map $\tau : (K_1, L_1) \to (K_2, L_2)$ a homomorphism of degree zero usually indicated by $\tau_* : H(K_1, L_1; G) \to H(K_2, L_2; G)$.

The groups $Z_q(K, L; G)$ and $B_{q-1}(K, L; G)$ are defined to be the kernel and image respectively of the homomorphism $\partial : C_q(K, L; G) \to C_{q-1}(K, L : G)$ so that $H_q(K, L; G) = Z_q(K, L; G)/B_q(K, L; G)$. An element of $Z_q(K, L; G)$ is called a relative cycle of $K \pmod L$. If L is the null complex we write $H_q(K; G)$ instead of $H_q(K, \varnothing; G)$ and the group $H_q(K; G)$ is called an *absolute* homology group.

EXERCISE 2

1. Prove that the morphism function, described in Example 9 by $T(f) = f \mid T(G)$, satisfies the definition of a covariant functor. Why are the morphisms required to be surjective?

2. Prove that the morphism function $||$ of Definition 5 satisfies the definition of a covariant functor.

3. Show that the composition of two covariant functors is a covariant functor.

4. Show that there is a category $\mathscr{A}$ of abelian pairs whose objects are ordered pairs (G, H) where G is an abelian group and H is a sub-group of G and whose morphisms from (G_1, H_1) to (G_2, H_2) are homomorphisms $f: (G_1, H_1) \to (G_2, H_2)$ from G_1 to G_2 which map H_1 into H_2.

5. Show that there is a covariant functor T from the category $\mathscr{A}$ (Problem 4) to the category of abelian groups such that $T(G, H)$ is the factor group G/H and whose morphism function is indicated by this commutative diagram.

$$\begin{array}{ccc} G_1/H_1 & \xrightarrow{\ T(f)\ } & G_2/H_2 \\ {\scriptstyle\Theta_1}\uparrow & & \uparrow{\scriptstyle\Theta_2} \\ G_1 & \xrightarrow{\ \ f\ \ } & G_2 \end{array}$$

6. Let (K, L) be a simplicial pair. Recall that $C_q(L; G)$ was identified with a subgroup of $C_q(K; G)$ by way of the injection $C_q(L; G) \to C_q(K; G)$. Show that this identification amounts to the definition

$$C_q(L; G) = \{c \in C_q(K; G) : s^q \notin L \Rightarrow c(s^q) = 0\}.$$

7. For the simplicial pair (K, L) consider the diagram

$$\begin{array}{ccc} C_q(K; G)/C_q(L; G) & \xrightarrow{\ \bar{\partial}_q\ } & C_{q-1}(K; G)/C_{q-1}(L; G) \\ {\scriptstyle\Theta_q}\uparrow & & \uparrow{\scriptstyle\Theta_{q-1}} \\ C_q(K; G) & \xrightarrow{\ \ \partial_q\ \ } & C_{q-1}(K; G) \end{array}$$

Recall that $C_q(K, L; G) = C_q(K; G)/C_q(L; G)$, $Z_q(K, L; G) = $ Kernel $(\bar{\partial}_q)$, $B_q(K, L; G) = $ Image$(\bar{\partial}_{q+1})$, and $H_q(K, L; G) = Z_q(K, L; G)/B_q(K, L; G)$. Show that

$$Z_q(K, L; G) = (\partial_{q-1}C_{q-1}(L; G) + C_q(L; G))/C_q(L; G)$$

$$B_q(K, L; G) = (\partial_{q+1}C_{q+1}(K; G) + C_q(L; G))/C_q(L; G).$$

8. Let K and L be the combinatorial closure and boundary of a 3-simplex as described in Problems 3 and 4, Exercise 5, Chapter I. Show that $Z_3(K, L; G)$ is isomorphic to G and $B_3(K, L; G) = 0$. Also, $Z_q(K, L; G) = 0$ for $q \neq 3$. Conclude that

$$H_q(K, L; G) \approx \begin{cases} G & \text{for } q = 3 \\ 0 & \text{for } q \neq 3. \end{cases}$$

3. QUOTIENT CATEGORIES

In the present section a study of certain relations in categories will provide a common setting for various situations which will be encountered later. The relations in question are set out in the following definition.

DEFINITION 10. A *morphism equivalence relation* in a category $\mathscr{K}$ is an equivalence relation $\mathscr{R}$ on the class of morphisms of $\mathscr{K}$ (written $f\mathscr{R}g$) satisfying the following conditions.

(1) $f\mathscr{R}g$ implies that f and g are elements of the same set $\text{Hom}(X, Y)$.

(2) If f_1 and g_1 are elements of $\text{Hom}(X, Y)$ and f_2 and g_2 are elements of $\text{Hom}(Y, Z)$, then $f_1\mathscr{R}g_1$ and $f_2\mathscr{R}g_2$ imply $f_2 f_1\mathscr{R}g_2 g_1$.

Condition (2) of Definition 10 is expressed by saying that composites of equivalent morphisms are equivalent.

DEFINITION 11. Let $\mathscr{R}$ be a morphism equivalence relation in a category $\mathscr{K}$. If $f \in \text{Hom}(X, Y)$, $g \in \text{Hom}(Y, X)$, and $(gf)\mathscr{R}I_X$, then g is called a left $\mathscr{R}$-inverse of f and f is called a right $\mathscr{R}$-inverse of g. If g is both a left and right $\mathscr{R}$-inverse of f, then f is called an $\mathscr{R}$-equivalence. If there exists an $\mathscr{R}$-equivalence in $\text{Hom}(X, Y)$, then X and Y are said to have the same $\mathscr{R}$-type or to be $\mathscr{R}$-equivalent.

THEOREM 6. Let $\mathscr{R}$ be a morphism equivalence relation in a category.

(a) If a morphism f has a left $\mathscr{R}$-inverse g_1 and a right $\mathscr{R}$-inverse g_2, there is a two sided $\mathscr{R}$-inverse of f equivalent to both g_1 and g_2.

(b) The relation of being $\mathscr{R}$-equivalent on the class of objects is reflexive, symmetric, and transitive.

Proof of (a): The morphism $g_1 f g_2$ is a two sided $\mathscr{R}$-inverse of f equivalent to both g_1 and g_2.

THEOREM 7. Let $\mathcal{R}_1$ and $\mathcal{R}_2$ be morphism equivalence relations in categories $\mathcal{K}_1$ and $\mathcal{K}_2$. Suppose that T is a covariant functor from $\mathcal{K}_1$ to $\mathcal{K}_2$ such that $f\mathcal{R}_1 g$ implies $T(f)\mathcal{R}_2 T(g)$. Then for each $\mathcal{R}_1$-equivalence f in $\mathcal{K}_1$, $T(f)$ is an $\mathcal{R}_2$-equivalence in $\mathcal{K}_2$. Therefore if objects X and Y are $\mathcal{R}_1$-equivalent in $\mathcal{K}_1$, then $T(X)$ and $T(Y)$ are $\mathcal{R}_2$-equivalent in $\mathcal{K}_2$.

Proof: Suppose that f is an element of $\mathrm{Hom}(X, Y)$ and that g is an $\mathcal{R}_1$-inverse of f. Then $(gf)\mathcal{R}_1 I_X$ implies $T(gf)\mathcal{R}_2 T(I_X)$. Consequently, $T(g)T(f)\mathcal{R}_2 I_{T(X)}$. A similar argument shows that $T(f)T(g)\mathcal{R}_2 I_{T(Y)}$.

THEOREM 8. For each morphism equivalence relation $\mathcal{R}$ in a category $\mathcal{K}$, there is a category (called a quotient category) $\mathcal{K}/\mathcal{R}$ whose objects are the objects of $\mathcal{K}$ and whose morphisms are the $\mathcal{R}$-equivalence classes of morphisms in $\mathcal{K}$.

4. THE HOMOTOPY CATEGORY

An example of a morphism equivalence is afforded by the relation of homotopy in the category of topological pairs and continuous maps. Some basic definitions and results regarding the homotopy relation will be recalled. The symbol I will be used to denote the closed unit interval of real numbers.

DEFINITION 12. Let f and g be maps of a topological pair (X, A) into a pair (Y, B). Then f is said to be *homotopic* to g (written $f \simeq g$) if there exists a map $F : (X \times I, A \times I) \to (Y, B)$ such that for each $x \in X$, $F(x, 0) = f(x)$ and $F(x, 1) = g(x)$. The map F is called a homotopy from f to g (written $F : f \simeq g$).

The map F of Definition 12 is sometimes said to deform the map f into the map g. For this reason, a homotopy is frequently called a *deformation*.

THEOREM 9. The homotopy relation is a morphism equivalence relation in the category of topological pairs and continuous maps.

Proof: To show that the homotopy relation is reflexive, observe that $F(x, t) = f(x)$ is a homotopy from f to f. For the symmetric property observe that if $F(x, t)$ is a homotopy from f to g, then $G(x, t) = F(x, 1 - t)$ is a homotopy from g to f. For the transitive property, assume that $F(x, t)$ is a homotopy from f to g and that $G(x, t)$ is a homotopy from g to h. Then the map $H : (X \times I, A \times I) \to (Y, B)$ given by

$$H(x, t) = \begin{cases} F(x, 2t) & 0 \leqslant t \leqslant 1/2 \\ G(x, 2t - 1) & 1/2 \leqslant t \leqslant 1 \end{cases}$$

is a homotopy from f to h.

The final item in the proof is to show that the composites of homotopic maps are homotopic. This can be done by observing that if $F : f \simeq f'$ and $G : g \simeq g'$ where $f, f' : (X, A) \to (Y, B)$ and $g, g' : (Y, B) \to (Z, C)$, then the map $H : (X \times I, A \times I) \to (Z, C)$ given by

$$H(x, t) = \begin{cases} gF(x, 2t) & 0 \leqslant t \leqslant 1/2 \\ G(f'(x), 2t - 1) & 1/2 \leqslant t \leqslant 1 \end{cases}$$

is a homotopy from gf to $g'f'$.

Having proved that the homotopy relation is a morphism equivalence relation, we have as a special case of Theorem 8 that there is a category whose objects are topological pairs and whose morphisms are homotopy classes of maps. Homotopically equivalent topological pairs are said to have the same *homotopy type*. It is the custom not to distinguish between a single space X and the pair $(X, \varnothing)$. It follows from this that the category of topological spaces is a subcategory of the category of topological pairs. It is with this understanding that we speak of spaces X and Y having the same homotopy type.

5. THE CHAIN HOMOTOPY CATEGORY

The definition is given here of a relation whose significance in the category of chain complexes is analogous to that of the homotopy relation in the category of topological pairs.

DEFINITION 13. Let τ and τ' be chain transformations from a chain complex C to a chain complex C'. A *chain homotopy* D from τ to τ' (written $D : \tau \simeq \tau'$) is a homomorphism $D = \{D_q\}$ of degree one from C to C' such that for each q

$$\partial'_{q+1} D_q + D_{q-1} \partial_q = \tau_q - \tau'_q.$$

According to this definition each D_q is a homomorphism from C_q to C'_{q+1}. If such a chain homotopy exists, then τ and τ' are said to be chain homotopic.

THEOREM 10. The chain homotopy relation is a morphism equivalence relation in the category of chain complexes.

Proof: It is trivial to show that chain homotopy is an equivalence relation on each set $\mathrm{Hom}(C, C')$.

To start the proof that composites of chain homotopic chain maps are chain homotopic assume that τ, τ' are elements of $\mathrm{Hom}(C, C')$, that σ, σ' are elements of $\mathrm{Hom}(C', C'')$, that $D : \tau \simeq \tau'$, and that $D' : \sigma \simeq \sigma'$. Then let $D'' = \{D''_q\}$ be the homomorphism of degree one from C to C'' given by $D''_q = \sigma_{q+1} D_q + D'_q \tau'_q$. Then we have

$$
\begin{aligned}
\partial''_{q+1} D''_q + D''_{q-1}\, \partial_q &= \partial''_{q+1}(\sigma_{q+1}D_q + D'_q\tau'_q) + (\sigma_q D_{q-1} + D'_{q-1}\tau'_{q-1})\,\partial_q \\
&= \sigma_q\, \partial'_{q+1}D_q + \partial''_{q+1}D'_q\tau'_q + \sigma_q D_{q-1}\,\partial_q + D'_{q-1}\,\partial'_q\tau'_q \\
&= \sigma_q(\partial'_{q+1}D_q + D_{q-1}\,\partial_q) + (\partial''_{q+1}D'_q + D'_{q-1}\,\partial_q)\tau'_q \\
&= \sigma_q(\tau_q - \tau'_q) + (\sigma_q - \sigma'_q)\tau'_q \\
&= \sigma_q\tau_q - \sigma'_q\tau'_q.
\end{aligned}
$$

This completes the proof of Theorem 10.

An important property of the chain homotopy relation is given in the next theorem. In the statement of this theorem, H is the homology functor of Theorem 5 and assigns to each chain complex C the graded homology group $H(C)$ and to each chain transformation α the induced homomorphism $H(\alpha)$.

THEOREM 11. If $\alpha, \beta : C \to C'$ are chain homotopic chain transformations, then $H(\alpha) = H(\beta)$.

Proof: Recall that $H(\alpha)$ was defined to make the following diagram commutative.

$$
\begin{array}{ccc}
H_q(C) & \xrightarrow{\ H_q(\alpha)\ } & H_q(C') \\
\theta_q \uparrow & & \uparrow \theta'_q \\
Z_q(C) & \longrightarrow & Z_q(C')
\end{array}
$$

Assume now that $D : \alpha \simeq \beta$ and consider an element c of $Z_q(C)$. Since $\partial_q(c) = 0$, then $\partial'_{q+1} D_q(c) = \alpha_q(c) - \beta_q(c)$. Consequently, $\alpha_q(c) - \beta_q(c) \in B_q(C')$ and it follows that $H_q(\alpha)(\theta_q(c)) = H_q(\beta)(\theta_q(c))$.

Having proved Theorem 10, there is a category whose objects are chain complexes and whose morphisms are chain homotopy classes of chain transformations as a special case of Theorem 8. As a consequence of Theorem 11, we see that the functor H can be regarded as a functor on this quotient category to the category of graded groups. Also, as a consequence of Theorem 7, graded homology groups of chain homotopy equivalent chain complexes are isomorphic.

6. THE CONTIGUITY CATEGORY

The objective in the present section is to define a morphism equivalence relation in the category of simplicial pairs and to work out certain results involving this relation and the relations of homotopy and chain homotopy.

DEFINITION 14. In the category of simplicial pairs let σ and τ be simplicial maps from (K_1, L_1) to (K_2, L_2). Then σ and τ are said to be *contiguous* provided for each simplex s^r in K_1 (or L_1), $\sigma(s^r)$ and $\tau(s^r)$ are faces of a common simplex in K_2 (or L_2). Both σ and τ are said to be in the same contiguity class provided there exists a finite sequence $\{\alpha_0, \alpha_1, \ldots, \alpha_p\}$ where each α_i is a simplicial map from (K_1, L_1) to (K_2, L_2), $\alpha_0 = \sigma$, $\alpha_p = \tau$, and α_i is contiguous to α_{i+1} for $i = 0, 1, \ldots, p - 1$.

THEOREM 12. The relation of being in the same contiguity class is a morphism equivalence relation in the category of simplicial pairs.

Proof: It is trivial to prove that the relation in question is an equivalence relation on the set of morphisms. To prove that composites of maps in the same contiguity class are in the same contiguity class, it is sufficient to consider maps which are actually contiguous. Suppose then that $\sigma, \sigma' : K_1 \rightarrow K_2$ are contiguous as are $\tau, \tau' : K_2 \rightarrow K_3$, and let s^r be a simplex in K_1. Then $\sigma(s^r)$ and $\sigma'(s^r)$ are faces of a simplex s^k in K_2. Also, $\tau(s^k)$ and $\tau'(s^k)$ are faces of a simplex s^p in K_3. It then follows that $\tau\sigma(s^r)$ and $\tau'\sigma'(s^r)$ are faces of s^p and consequently $\tau\sigma$ and $\tau'\sigma'$ are contiguous.

Two important properties of the contiguity relation are given next. The symbol | | is used to represent the functor of Definition 5 which assigns to each simplicial pair (K, L) the topological pair $(|K|, |L|)$ and to each simplicial map σ the continuous map $|\sigma|$. The symbol C will represent the functor of Theorem 3 which assigns to each simplicial pair (K, L) the chain complex $C(K, L; G)$.

THEOREM 13. If $\sigma, \tau : (K_1, L_1) \to (K_2, L_2)$ are simplicial maps in the same contiguity class, then $|\sigma|$ and $|\tau|$ are homotopic.

Proof: Again, it will be sufficient to consider the case where σ and τ are actually contiguous. Then for each element x of $|K_1|$, $|\sigma|(x)$ and $|\tau|(x)$ are elements of the closure of a simplex s^r of K_2 and this simplex s^r is in L_2 if x is an element of $|L_1|$. Since the segment $\langle|\sigma|(x), |\tau|(x)\rangle$ is contained in the closure of s^r, a homotopy from $|\sigma|$ to $|\tau|$ may be defined by $H(x, t) = (1 - t)|\sigma|(x) + t|\tau|(x)$.

THEOREM 14. If $\sigma, \tau : (K_1, L_1) \to (K_2, L_2)$ are simplicial maps in the same contiguity class, then $C(\sigma)$ and $C(\tau)$ are chain homotopic.

Proof: The proof will be given only for the case $L_1 = L_2 = \emptyset$, the modifications for the general case being fairly obvious. Furthermore, it will be sufficient to consider only the case where σ and τ are actually contiguous. The hypothesis of contiguity permits the definition of homomorphisms $D_r : C_r(K_1; G) \to C_{r+1}(K_2; G)$ as follows. First, for each oriented simplex $s^r = \langle a_0, a_1, \ldots, a_r \rangle$ in K_1, $D_r(s^r)$ is defined as the integral $(r + 1)$-chain of K_2 given by

$$D_r(s^r) = \sum (-1)^i \langle \sigma(a_0), \sigma(a_1), \ldots, \sigma(a_i), \tau(a_i), \ldots, \tau(a_r) \rangle.$$

In this definition it is agreed that any summand involving repeated vertices has the value zero. In order to extend the definition of D_r to $C_r(K_1; G)$, write $D_r(\sum g^i s_i^r) = \sum g^i D_r(s_i^r)$. When the expression

$$\partial_{r+1} D_r(s^r) + D_{r-1} \partial_r(s^r)$$

is written out, all terms cancel except

$$\langle \tau(a_0), \tau(a_1), \ldots, \tau(a_r) \rangle - \langle \sigma(a_0), \sigma(a_1), \ldots, \sigma(a_r) \rangle.$$

Hence
$$\partial_{r+1} D_r(s^r) + D_{r-1}\, \partial_r(s^r) = C(\tau)(s^r) - C(\sigma)(s^r);$$
then by the linearity of the definition of D_r,
$$\partial_{r+1} D_r + D_{r-1}\, \partial_r = C(\tau) - C(\sigma).$$
This proves that D is a chain homotopy from $C(\tau)$ to $C(\sigma)$.

The information developed here about the contiguity relation can be summarized by saying that there is a category whose objects are simplicial pairs and whose morphisms are contiguity classes of simplicial maps and that the functors $|\ |$ and C may be considered to be functors on this category. In particular, if $\tau : (K_1, L_1) \to (K_2, L_2)$ is a contiguity equivalence, then $(|K_1|, |L_1|)$ and $(|K_2|, |L_2|)$ have the same homotopy type and $C(K_1, L_1; G)$ is chain homotopy equivalent to $C(K_2, L_2; G)$. Also, if $\sigma, \tau : (K_1, L_1) \to (K_2, L_2)$ are simplicial maps in the same contiguity class, then the chain transformations $C(\sigma)$ and $C(\tau)$ are chain homotopic so that by Theorem 11 the homomorphisms $\sigma_*, \tau_* : H(K_1, L_1; G) \to H(K_2, L_2; G)$ are identical.

EXERCISE 3

For purposes of this exercise let K be the combinatorial closure of an n-simplex $s^n = \Delta(a_0, a_1, \ldots, a_n)$ and let L be the subcomplex consisting of the single vertex a_0. Let $\sigma : K \to K$ be the identity simplicial map; that is, $\sigma(a_i) = a_i$ for each i. Let $\tau : K \to K$ be the constant simplicial map given by $\tau(a_i) = a_0$. Prove each of the following statements.

1. $|\sigma|$ is the identity map of $|K|$.

2. $|\tau|$ maps $|K|$ into the point a_0.

3. σ and τ are in the same contiguity class so that $|\sigma|$ and $|\tau|$ are homotopic.

4. The constant map $|K| \to |L|$ is a homotopy equivalence. This last statement is expressed by saying that $|K|$ has the homotopy type of a point.

5. The complex K and the complex L are equivalent objects in the contiguity category.

6. The graded homology group $H(L; G)$ is given by
$$H_q(L; G) \approx \begin{cases} G & \text{if } q = 0 \\ 0 & \text{if } q \neq 0. \end{cases}$$

7. The graded homology groups $H(K; G)$ and $H(L; G)$ are isomorphic.

7. SIMPLICIAL APPROXIMATIONS

In the category of polytopes, each object X is the space of some complex K and we write $X = |K|$. In the applications of algebraic topology one deduces topological properties of the polytope X from algebraic properties of K. Likewise, in the transition from polytopes to complexes, continuous functions $f: |K| \to |L|$ must be replaced by simplicial maps $\tau: K \to L$. Although not every continuous function $f: |K| \to |L|$ can be written $f = |\tau|$ for some simplicial map τ, it is true that in a certain sense each polytope map $f: X \to Y$ can be approximated by a simplicial map. The next definition is the first step in working out this idea.

> DEFINITION 15.   Let K be a complex. For each vertex a of K, define the *closed star* of a to be the collection of all simplexes of K having a as a vertex and all faces of such simplexes. The *star* of a, written star(a), is the union of all simplexes of K having a as a vertex.

For each vertex a of K, the closed star of a is a subcomplex of K, while the star of a is an open set in the polytope $|K|$. The collection of stars is an open covering of $|K|$. There is a very useful characterization of the set of vertices of a simplex in terms of stars.

> LEMMA 1.   A set of vertices $\{a_0, a_1, \ldots, a_r\}$ of a complex K is the set of vertices of a simplex if and only if the set $\bigcap_{i=0}^{r} \{\text{star}(a_i)\}$ is not null.

The proof is left as an exercise.

> DEFINITION 16.   Let $f: |K| \to |L|$ be a map. Then the complex K is said to be star related to L with respect to the map f if, for each vertex a of K, there exists a vertex b of L such that f maps the star of a into the star of b. If $\tau: K \to L$ is a simplicial map such that, for each vertex a of K, f maps the star of a into the star of $\tau(a)$, then τ is called a simplicial approximation of f.

THEOREM 15. (a) If K is star related to L with respect to a map f, then there exists a simplicial approximation $\tau : K \to L$ of f.

(b) Composites of simplicial approximations are simplicial approximations.

Proof of (a): For each vertex a of K, select a vertex $\tau(a)$ of L such that f maps the star of a into the star of $\tau(a)$. To show that the vertex mapping τ thus defined is actually a simplicial map, consider a simplex $\Delta(a_0, a_1, \ldots, a_r)$ of K. The image under f of the nonnull set $\cap\{\text{star}(a_i)\}$ is contained in the set $\cap\{\text{star } \tau(a_i)\}$, which implies that this last set is also nonnull, and we infer by Lemma 1 that the $\tau(a_i)$ are vertices of a simplex in L. This is sufficient to prove that the function τ is a simplicial approximation of f.

The simplicial approximation of Theorem 15 is, in general, not unique since for a given vertex a of K there may exist many choices for the vertex b. We do, however, have the following result.

THEOREM 16. Let $\sigma, \tau : K \to L$ be simplicial maps. If σ and τ are simplicial approximations of the same map, then they are contiguous.

Proof: Let σ and τ be simplicial approximations of a map $f : |K| \to |L|$ and let $s^r = \Delta(a_0, a_1, \ldots, a_r)$ be a simplex of K. Then the nonnull set $f(s^r)$ is contained in the set $(\cap\{\text{star } \sigma(a_i)\}) \cap (\cap\{\text{star } \tau(a_i)\})$. It follows that the vertices $\sigma(a_i)$ and $\tau(a_i)$ are vertices of a simplex in L.

8. SUBDIVISIONS

If $f : |K| \to |L|$ is a continuous function, then K may not be star related to L with respect to f and in this case, there will be no simplicial approximation $\tau : K \to L$ of f. We shall see however that there always exists a complex K' such that $|K'| = |K|$ and K' is star related to L with respect to f. Ideas such as these lead to the constructions in this section.

DEFINITION 17. A complex K' is said to be a *subdivision* of a complex K provided the following conditions are satisfied.

(i) $|K| = |K'|$.

(ii) Each simplex of K' is contained in a simplex of K.

It is easy to see that if K' is a subdivision of K, then each simplex of K is the union of those simplexes of K' which it contains. The next proposition is an immediate consequence of the definition.

THEOREM 17. Let K' be a subdivision of K. Then K' is star related to K with respect to the identity map $i : |K'| \to |K|$.

Proof: Let b be a vertex of K' and it must be shown that there exists a vertex a of K such that star(b) is contained in star(a). The vertex b of K' is contained in a simplex $\Delta(a_0, a_1, \ldots, a_r)$ of K and thus star(b) is contained in each star(a_i) $i = 0, 1, \ldots, r$. To see that this is so, recall that star(b) is the union of all simplexes of K' having b as a vertex. Let s^t be one such simplex. Now s^t is contained in a simplex s^q of K. Next, the point b is an element of the closure of s^t which is contained in the closure of s^q. Finally, we have by Theorem 7, Chapter I that $\Delta(a_0, a_1, \ldots, a_r)$ is a face of s^q. In other words, each a_i is a vertex of s^q and s^q is therefore contained in star(a_i), and the proof is complete.

COROLLARY. Suppose that K' is a subdivision of K and $\tau : K' \to K$ is a vertex mapping such that for each vertex b of K', $\tau(b)$ is a vertex of the simplex in K containing b. Then τ is a simplicial approximation of the identity.

In the applications we always need to know that there are subdivisions satisfying certain conditions. The next step is to prove the existence of subdivisions that decompose a given complex into arbitrarily small pieces. It will be shown that there is associated with each complex K the so-called barycentric subdivision K'.

DEFINITION 18. The *centroid* or *barycenter* of a simplex $s^r = \Delta(a_0, a_1, \ldots, a_r)$ is that point p of s^r all of whose barycentric coordinates are equal. In other words, $p = 1/(r + 1) \sum a_i$.

The next two theorems are concerned with the following construction. Let K be a complex which is the combinatorial closure of a simplex s^n and we wish to exhibit a special subdivision K' of K. K' will be an n-dimensional complex and one of its n-simplexes may be described as follows. First assign an order $a_0, a_1, \ldots, a_n$ to the vertices of s^n and for each $r, 0 \leqslant r \leqslant n$; let p_r be the centroid of the simplex $\Delta(a_0, a_1, \ldots, a_r)$.

THEOREM 18. The set $\{p_0, p_1, \ldots, p_n\}$ is geometrically independent.

Proof: Each point p_j is an element of $\pi(a_0, a_1, \ldots, a_n)$ so we may write $p_j = \sum \lambda_j^i a_i$ where $\{\lambda_j^i\}$ are the barycentric coordinates of the p_j. The matrix (λ_j^i) has the form

$$\begin{pmatrix} 1 & 0 & 0 & \cdots & 0 \\ 1/2 & 1/2 & 0 & \cdots & 0 \\ 1/3 & 1/3 & 1/3 & \cdots & 0 \\ \cdot & \cdot & \cdot & \cdots & \cdot \\ 1/n+1 & \cdot & \cdot & \cdots & 1/n+1 \end{pmatrix}.$$

Since this matrix is nonsingular, it follows that the set $\{p_0, p_1, \ldots, p_n\}$ is geometrically independent and therefore spans an n-dimensional simplex. The symbol K' will denote the set of all nonnull faces of n-simplexes so constructed. Note that the first step in constructing one of these n-simplexes is the selection of an ordering of the set of vertices of s^n and each different ordering leads to a different n-simplex. Therefore the set K' contains $(n + 1)!$ n-simplexes. The next theorem will show that K' is actually a complex of dimension n.

THEOREM 19. K' is a subdivision of K.

Proof: First, to show that each point of $|K|$ belongs to at least one simplex of K', choose an element x of $|K|$ and let $\{a_0, a_1, \ldots, a_n\}$ be the vertices of s^n arranged in such an order that the corresponding barycentric coordinates $\{\lambda^0, \lambda^1, \ldots, \lambda^n\}$ of x form a nonincreasing sequence. Now let

$$p_r = (1/1 + r) \sum_{i=0}^{r} a_i \qquad \text{for } 0 \leq r \leq n.$$

It is easy to see that

$$x = \sum_{i=0}^{n} \lambda^i a_i = \sum_{r=0}^{n-1} (r + 1)(\lambda^r - \lambda^{r+1})p_r + (n + 1)\lambda^n p_n$$

and that

$$\sum_{r=0}^{n-1} (r + 1)(\lambda^r - \lambda^{r+1}) + (n + 1)\lambda^n = 1.$$

This proves that x is an element of the simplex spanned by those p_r for which $\lambda^r > \lambda^{r+1}$.

We wish to show next that each element x of $|K|$ belongs to a unique simplex of K'. Suppose then that x is an element of the simplex of K' whose vertices are $\{q_0, q_1, \ldots, q_r\}$. This simplex arises in the following manner. There is an ordering $\{a_0, a_1, \ldots, a_n\}$ of the vertices of s^n such that each vertex q_i is one of the elements of the set $\{p_0, p_1, \ldots, p_n\}$ where for each i,

$$p_i = \frac{1}{i + 1}\left(\sum_{j=0}^{i} a_j\right).$$

Now let $\{\mu^0, \mu^1, \ldots, \mu^n\}$ be the barycentric coordinates of x with respect to $\{p_0, p_1, \ldots, p_n\}$. We then have that

$$x = \sum_{i=0}^{n} \left(\sum_{j=i}^{n} \mu^j/j + 1\right)a_i.$$

In other words, the barycentric coordinates of x with respect to the set $\{a_0, a_1, \ldots, a_n\}$ are given by

(2) $$\lambda^i = \sum_{j=i}^{n} (\mu^j/j + 1).$$

It follows that $\lambda^i \geqslant \lambda^{i+1}$ and $\lambda^i = \lambda^{i+1}$ if and only if $\mu^i = 0$. Therefore, the points $q_0, q_1, \ldots, q_r$ may be characterized as those p_i for which $\lambda^i > \lambda^{i+1}$. This means that the set $\{q_0, q_1, \ldots, q_r\}$ is uniquely determined by the point x and x is an element of a unique simplex of K'.

Equation (2) will also take care of the final step in the proof which is to show that each simplex $s^r = \Delta(q_0, q_1, \ldots, q_r)$ of K' is contained in some simplex of K. Again, there is an ordering $\{a_0, a_1, \ldots, a_n\}$ of the vertices of s^n such that each q_i is one of the associated barycenters $\{p_0, p_1, \ldots, p_n\}$. There is an integer $k = \max\{i : p_i = q_j \text{ for some } j\}$. Again, let

$\{\mu^i\}$ be barycentric coordinates with respect to $\{p_0, p_1, \ldots, p_n\}$ and for $x \in s^r$, $\mu^i(x) = 0$ for $i > k$ and $\mu^k(x) > 0$. Using this and Equation (2) we see that for $x \in s^r$, $\lambda^i(x) = 0$ if and only if $i > k$. This proves that s^r is contained in the face $\Delta(a_0, a_1, \ldots, a_k)$ of s^n.

> DEFINITION 19. The complex K' described above is called the *barycentric subdivision* of the simplex s^n. More generally, the barycentric subdivision of a complex K, denoted by $K^{(1)}$, is defined as the union of the barycentric subdivisions of the simplexes of K. The complex $K^{(n)}$, called the nth barycentric subdivision of K, is defined to be the barycentric subdivision of $K^{(n-1)}$ for $n > 1$.

9. EXISTENCE OF SIMPLICIAL APPROXIMATIONS

It has already been suggested that the importance of the concept of a subdivision is related to the necessity of proving that simplicial approximations of continuous functions actually exist. According to Theorem 15, a continuous function $f : |K| \to |L|$ has a simplicial approximation $\tau : K \to L$ if and only if K is star related to L with respect to f. A more convenient formulation of this result can be given and the next definition is a first step in this direction.

> DEFINITION 20. Let $\mathcal{U}$ be an open covering of a polytope X and let K be a triangulation of X. That is, K is a simplicial complex and $|K| = X$. The triangulation K is said to be *finer* than the covering $\mathcal{U}$ if, for each vertex a of K, the star of a is contained in some open set of the covering $\mathcal{U}$.

The question of the existence of simplicial approximations is related to the question of the existence of triangulations finer than a given open covering. A triangulation K will be finer than a given open covering provided the maximum diameter of simplexes in K is small enough. In this connection we have the following definition and theorem.

DEFINITION 21. The *mesh* of a complex K is the maximum diameter of simplexes in K.

THEOREM 20. For a given complex K, the mesh of $K^{(n)}$ approaches zero as n approaches infinity.

Two lemmas will be used in the proof of Theorem 20.

LEMMA 2. The diameter of a simplex s^n is the maximum distance between vertices of s^n.

Proof: Let q be a point of s^n and let d be the distance from q to the most distant vertex p. The sphere of radius d and center q contains all vertices of s^n and therefore contains s^n. This means that the most distant point from q is a vertex. Consequently, if the distance between q and p is a maximum, each is a vertex.

LEMMA 3. Let s^t be a simplex of the first barycentric subdivision of a simplex $s^n = \Delta(a_0, a_1, \ldots, a_n)$. The diameter of s^t is less than or equal to $(n/(n + 1))u$ where u is the diameter of s^n.

Proof: Let p and q be vertices of s^t, a simplex in the first barycentric subdivision of a simplex $s^n = \Delta(a_0, a_1, \ldots, a_n)$. We may suppose that

$$p = \frac{1}{r}\left(\sum_{i=0}^{r-1} a_i\right), \qquad q = \frac{1}{t}\left(\sum_{j=0}^{t-1} a_j\right), \qquad 0 \le t < r \le n.$$

Then

$$p - q = \frac{1}{r}\left(\sum_{i=0}^{r-1}\{a_i - q\}\right)$$

$$a_i - q = \frac{1}{t}\left(\sum_{j=0}^{t-1}\{a_i - a_j\}\right)$$

$$p - q = \frac{1}{rt}\left(\sum_{i=0}^{r-1}\sum_{j=0}^{t-1}\{a_i - a_j\}\right).$$

Now let $|p - q|$ represent the distance from p to q and we have

$$|p - q| \leq \frac{1}{rt} \left(\sum_{i=0}^{r-1} \sum_{j=0}^{t-1} |a_i - a_j| \right) \leq \left(\frac{rt - t}{rt} \right) u$$

$$\leq \left(\frac{r - 1}{r} \right) u \leq \left(\frac{n}{n + 1} \right) u.$$

The proof of Theorem 20 now follows easily.

The results of Theorem 20 are related to the question of the existence of simplicial approximations through the notion of a *Lebesgue number* of an open covering.

THEOREM 21. Let $\mathscr{U}$ be an open covering of a compact metric space X. There exists a number $\delta > 0$ (called a Lebesgue number of the covering $\mathscr{U}$) such that each subset of X having diameter less than δ is contained in some open set of the covering $\mathscr{U}$.

The proof of Theorem 21 is left as an exercise.

We are finally in a position to prove the principal result of this section.

THEOREM 22. Let $f : |K| \to |L|$ be a continuous function. For some positive integer n, the subdivision $K^{(n)}$ of K is star related to L with respect to f.

Proof: Consider the open covering $\mathscr{U}$ of K consisting of all sets of the form $f^{-1}(V)$ where V is the star of some vertex of L. Let δ be a Lebesgue number of $\mathscr{U}$. By Theorem 20 there exists an integer n such that the mesh of $K^{(n)}$ is less than $\delta/2$. Consequently, for each vertex a of K, the star of a is contained in some set $f^{-1}(V)$ and hence K is star related to L with respect to f.

COROLLARY. Let $f : |K| \to |L|$ be a continuous function. For some positive integer n, there exists a simplicial approximation $\tau : K^{(n)} \to L$ of f.

EXERCISE 4

1. Prove Lemma 1.

2. Prove Theorem 15(b).

3. Prove Theorem 21.

4. Let K and L be complexes such that $|K|$ and $|L|$ are respectively the boundaries of a triangle and of a square. Let $h : |K| \to |L|$ be a homeomorphism and show that there exists no simplicial approximation $\sigma : K \to L$ of h.

5. Let K be the combinatorial boundary of a 2-simplex. Show that there are 27 simplicial maps $K \to K$ and there are 7 contiguity classes of such maps.

10. INVARIANCE OF HOMOLOGY GROUPS UNDER BARYCENTRIC SUBDIVISION

In this section the plan is to establish the result that if K' is a subdivision of K, then the graded homology groups $H(K; G)$ and $H(K'; G)$ are isomorphic. Actually the result is stated for simplicial pairs so let us suppose that (K, L) is a simplicial pair and that K' and L' are the first barycentric subdivisions of K and L. Then (K', L') is a simplicial pair called the first barycentric subdivision of the pair (K, L). Since K' is star related to K with respect to the identity map, there exists a simplicial approximation $\tau : (K', L') \to (K, L)$ of the identity map. As in the statement of Theorem 3, there is for each coefficient group G a functor C which assigns to this simplicial approximation of the identity the chain transformation $C(\tau): C(K', L'; G) \to C(K, L; G)$. It will be shown that $C(\tau)$ is a chain homotopy equivalence by exhibiting a chain transformation $\zeta : C(K, L; G) \to C(K', L'; G)$ which is a chain homotopy inverse of $C(\tau)$. The proof will be given only for the case $L = L' = \emptyset$. The extension to the general case is easy.

The definition of the chain transformation ζ will require the notion of a cone complex.

DEFINITION 22. Let K be a simplicial complex. A cone complex over K with vertex p (indicated by the symbol $p * K$) is a complex whose simplexes are those of K and simplexes of the form $\Delta(p, a_0, a_1, \ldots, a_r)$ where $\{a_0, a_1, \ldots, a_r\}$ is the set of vertices of a simplex in K. In particular, the vertices of $p * K$ are the vertices of K and the point p. For each oriented r-simplex $s^r = \langle a_0, a_1, \ldots, a_r \rangle$ of K, the symbol $p * s^r$ represents the oriented $(r + 1)$-simplex of $p * K$ given by $p * s^r = \langle p, a_0, a_1, \ldots, a_r \rangle$. For each r-chain $c = \sum g^i s^r_i$ of K, $p * c$ is the $(r + 1)$-chain of $p * K$ given by $p * c = \sum g^i (p * s^r_i)$.

LEMMA 4. Let $p * K$ be a cone complex over K. Then for each $c \in C_q(K; G)$ $(q > 0)$, $\partial_{q+1}(p * c) = c - p * \partial_q(c)$.

The proof is made by observing that the conclusion holds, first of all, for the case where $c = s^q$ is an oriented q-simplex of K. The proof for the general case is then obtained by additivity.

We are now going to assume that K' is the first barycentric subdivision of a complex K and define, for each nonnegative dimension q, a homomorphism

$$\zeta_q : C_q(K; G) \to C_q(K'; G).$$

The definition will be made inductively.

DEFINITION 23. For each vertex a_i of K, define $\zeta_0(a_i) = a_i$. This definition is extended additively to a unique homomorphism $\zeta_0 : C_0(K; G) \to C_0(K'; G)$. Assume inductively that $\zeta_i : C_i(K; G) \to C_i(K'; G)$ has been defined for $i = 0, 1, \ldots, r - 1$. Then for each elementary integral r-chain s^r_j of K the definition of $\zeta_r(s^r_j)$ is made as follows. Let $\bar{s}^r_j$ be the complex consisting of the barycentric subdivisions of all $(r - 1)$-dimensional faces of s^r_j. Then the first barycentric subdivision of s^r_j is a cone complex over $\bar{s}^r_j$ with vertex p^r_j where p^r_j is the barycenter of $\bar{s}^r_j$. The chain $\zeta_r(s^r_j)$ is now defined by $\zeta_r(s^r_j) = p^r_j * \zeta_{r-1} \partial_r(s^r_j)$. This definition is extended additively to a unique homomorphism

$$\zeta_r : C_r(K; G) \to C_r(K'; G).$$

THEOREM 23. The sequence $\{\zeta_q\}$ of homomorphisms given in Definition 23 is a chain transformation from $C(K; G)$ to $C(K'; G)$.

Proof: It must be shown that $\partial'_q \zeta_q = \zeta_{q-1} \partial_q$ and this is trivially true for $q = 0$. Assume that $\partial'_{r-1} \zeta_{r-1} = \zeta_{r-2} \partial_{r-1}$. In particular, we have for each elementary integral r-chain s^r_j of K,

$$\partial'_r \zeta_r(s^r_j) = \partial'_r(p^r_j * \zeta_{r-1} \partial_r(s^r_j))$$
$$= \zeta_{r-1} \partial_r(s^r_j) - p^r_j * \partial'_{r-1} \zeta_{r-1} \partial_r(s^r_j)$$
$$= \zeta_{r-1} \partial_r(s^r_j) - p^r_j * \zeta_{r-2} \partial_{r-1} \partial_r(s^r_j) = \zeta_{r-1} \partial_r(s^r_j).$$

It then follows by additivity that $\partial'_r \zeta_r = \zeta_{r-1} \partial_r$ and the proof is complete.

Let us now assume, in addition to the agreements made earlier regarding K and K', that we have under consideration a definite map $\tau : K' \to K$ which is a simplicial approximation of the identity. It will be shown that the chain transformation $\zeta : C(K; G) \to C(K'; G)$ is a chain homotopy inverse of the chain transformation $C(\tau)$. First it will be shown that for each dimension q, ζ_q is a right inverse of $C_q(\tau)$. In other words, ζ is a right inverse of $C(\tau)$; hence it is certainly a right chain homotopy inverse. This is the content of the next theorem.

First we have a characterization of the subdivision homomorphism which will be convenient to use here and in the material that follows. To begin, let $\langle a_0, a_1 \rangle$ be an oriented 1-simplex with centroid p^1. We say that the oriented 1-simplexes $\langle a_0, p^1 \rangle$ and $\langle p^1, a_1 \rangle$ are oriented *like* $\langle a_0, a_1 \rangle$, and that $\langle p^1, a_0 \rangle$ and $\langle a_1, p^1 \rangle$ are oriented *unlike* $\langle a_0, a_1 \rangle$. Now suppose that K is the combinatorial closure of an oriented r-simplex s^r ($r > 1$), K' its first barycentric subdivision, s^{r-1} a face of s^r with the orientation it inherits from s^r, and t^{r-1} is an $(r-1)$-simplex of K' contained in s^{r-1}. Finally let p^r be the centroid of s^r. Then $p^r * t^{r-1}$ is an oriented simplex of K' contained in s^r and we say that $p^r * t^{r-1}$ is oriented like s^r provided t^{r-1} is oriented like s^{r-1}.

LEMMA 5. In the notation of the preceding paragraph, $\zeta_r(s^r) = \sum n_j t^r_j$ where the sum is over all r-simplexes of K', $n_j = +1$ if t^r_j is oriented like s^r, and $n_j = -1$ if t^r_j is oriented unlike s^r.

Proof: Suppose the lemma true for dimensions $0, 1, \ldots, r-1$. Then $\zeta_r(s^r) = p^r * \zeta_{r-1} \partial_r(s^r) = p^r * \sum n_j t^{r-1}_j = \sum n_j(p^r * t^{r-1}_j)$. Here the sums are over all t_j^{r-1} contained in the boundary of s^r, and in the first sum we see by the inductive hypothesis that $n_j = +1$ if and only if the orientation of t_j^{r-1} is like that inherited from s^r by its face containing t_j^{r-1}. This is equivalent to saying that $n_j = +1$ if and only if $p^r * t_j^{r-1}$ is oriented like s^r.

THEOREM 24. For $q \geqslant 0$, $C_q(\tau)\zeta_q = I_{C_q(K; G)}$.

Proof: Again the proof is by induction on q and the result is trivially true for $q = 0$. Now make the inductive hypothesis that $C_{r-1}(\tau)\zeta_{r-1}$ is the identity mapping of $C_{r-1}(K; G)$, and let us examine $C_r(\tau)\zeta_r(s_i^r)$ for a fixed elementary integral r-chain s_i^r of K. In the first place, $\zeta_r(s_i^r) = \sum n_j t_j^r$ where the sum is taken over all simplexes t_j^r of K' which are contained in s_i^r. Also, for each t_j^r contained in s_i^r, $C_r(\tau)(t_j^r) = \varepsilon_j s_i^r$ where $\varepsilon_j = \pm 1$ if τ does not collapse t_j^r and $\varepsilon_j = 0$ if τ collapses t_j^r. Consequently, $C_r(\tau)\zeta_r(s_i^r) = (\sum \varepsilon_j n_j)s_i^r = m_i s_i^r$ where m_i is an integer. Using the inductive hypothesis we infer from this that $m_i(\partial_r s_i^r) = \partial_r(m_i s_i^r) = \partial_r C_r(\tau)\zeta_r(s_i^r) = C_{r-1}(\tau)\zeta_{r-1}(\partial_r s_i^r) = \partial_r s_i^r$. Now since $\partial_r s_i^r$ is a nonzero chain, $m_i = 1$ and $C_r(\tau)\zeta_r(s_i^r) = s_i^r$. It follows that $C_r(\tau)\zeta_r = $ identity, and the proof is complete.

The proof of Theorem 24 having been completed, the remaining item for the present section is the proof that ζ is a left chain homotopy inverse of $C(\tau)$. Some preliminary material must be developed for this purpose. In the category of topological spaces and continuous functions a morphism which transforms its domain into a single point is considered to be trivial or "inessential." A topological space whose identity map is homotopic to an inessential map is said to be *contractible*. The analogy between this situation and the next definition is quite clear.

DEFINITION 24. A chain complex $C = \{C_q, \partial_q\}$ is said to be contractible provided the identity chain transformation of C is chain homotopic to the transformation which maps each C_q into the zero element of C_q.

DEFINITION 25. A chain complex C is said to be *acyclic* provided $H_q(C) = 0$ for each dimension q. The chain complex is said to be acyclic in dimension q if only $H_q(C) = 0$.

THEOREM 25. A contractible chain complex is acyclic.

The proof is left as an exercise.

THEOREM 26. For each cone complex $p * K$, the chain complex $C(p * K; G)$ is acyclic in each positive dimension.

Proof: It will be shown that $C(p * K; G)$ is chain homotopy equivalent to the chain complex $\bar{C}$ defined by

$$\bar{C}_q = \begin{cases} G & \text{for } q = 0 \\ 0 & \text{for } q \neq 0. \end{cases}$$

In this chain complex each ∂_q is the zero homomorphism and clearly $H(\bar{C}) = \bar{C}$. Let $\alpha : p * K \to p * K$ and $\beta : p * K \to p * K$ be respectively the identity simplicial mapping and the simplicial mapping which takes each vertex of $p * K$ into the vertex p. Now consider chain transformations $\text{In} : C(p * K; G) \to \bar{C}$ and $h : \bar{C} \to C(p * K; G)$ defined as follows. For $c \in C_0(p * K; G)$, $\text{In}_0(c)$ is the Kronecker index of c (Definition 22, Chapter I). For an element g of $G = \bar{C}_0$, $h(g) = gp$. In other words, $h(g)$ is the chain which assigns the group element g to the vertex p and zero to every other vertex. Now it is easy to see that the composition $\text{In} \cdot h$ is the identity map of $\bar{C}$ and that $h \cdot \text{In} = C(\beta)$. Notice next that α and β are contiguous so that $C(\alpha)$ and $C(\beta)$ are chain homotopic and that $C(\alpha)$ is the identity transformation of $C(p * K; G)$. Thus $h \cdot \text{In}$ is chain homotopic to the identity and we have that h and In are chain homotopy inverses of each other. This implies that $\bar{C}$ and $C(p * K; G)$ are chain homotopy equivalent. It follows that $H_q(p * K; G)$ is isomorphic to $H_q(\bar{C})$ and consequently $H_q(p * K; G) = 0$ for $q > 0$.

Since a complex M, which is the first barycentric subdivision of a simplex s^r, is a cone complex over the barycentric subdivision of the boundary of s^r, Theorem 26 has the following consequence.

COROLLARY. Let M be a complex which is the first barycentric subdivision of a complex K consisting of all nonnull faces of a simplex s^r. Then for each coefficient group G, the chain complex $C(M) = \{C_q(M), \partial_q\}$ is acyclic in all positive dimensions.

In the applications the acyclicity of $C(M)$ will be used in the following way. Since $H_q(M; G) = Z_q(M; G)/B_q(M; G) = 0$, it follows that each cycle in $Z_q(M; G)$ is a bounding cycle. In other words, for each $z \in Z_q(M; G)$ there exists a chain $c \in C_{q+1}(M; G)$ such that $\partial_{q+1}(c) = z$.

THEOREM 27. Let $\zeta : C(K; G) \to C(K'; G)$ and $C(\tau) : C(K'; G) \to C(K; G)$ be the subdivision homomorphism and the homomorphism induced by a simplicial approximation of the identity $|K'| \to |K|$ where K' is the first barycentric subdivision of the complex K. Then ζ is a left chain homotopy inverse of $C(\tau)$.

Proof: We make a dimension-by-dimension proof of the existence of a homotopy $D = \{D_q : C_q(K'; G) \to C_{q+1}(K'; G)\}$ from $\zeta C(\tau)$ to the identity transformation. Observe that for each subcomplex L of K, the first barycentric subdivision L' is a subcomplex of K' and the chain transformation $\zeta C(\tau)$ maps $C(L'; G)$ into itself. For this reason it will be convenient to work with the collection $\mathscr{L}$ of all complexes which are first barycentric subdivisions of subcomplexes of K. The inductive hypothesis we are going to make is that for each complex L' in $\mathscr{L}$ and for each coefficient group G a homomorphism

$$D_q : C_q(L'; G) \to C_{q+1}(L'; G)$$

has been defined for $q = 0, 1, \ldots, r - 1$ such that

$$\partial_{q+1} D_q(c^q) + D_{q-1} \partial_q(c^q) = \zeta_q C_q(\tau)(c^q) - c^q \text{ for } q > 0$$
$$\partial_1 D_0(c^0) = \zeta_0 C_0(\tau)(c^0) - c^0.$$

In order to make the definition of D_q for the next dimension r, we proceed as follows. Each oriented simplex t_i^r of K' is contained in a unique simplex s_i^n of K. Let M_i be the complex which is the first barycentric subdivision of s_i^n. We have the following diagram.

The homomorphisms indicated by the vertical arrows are the mappings $\zeta_q C_q(\tau)$ for $q = r$ and $r - 1$. Returning to the oriented simplex t_i^r, we have

$$\partial_r D_{r-1} \partial_r(t_i^r) = \zeta_{r-1} C_{r-1}(\tau) \partial_r(t_i^r) - \partial_r(t_i^r).$$

Consequently $\partial_r\{\zeta_r\, C_r(\tau)(t_i^r) - t_i^r - D_{r-1}\, \partial_r(t_i^r)\} = 0$. Now since $C(M_i\,;\,Z)$ is acyclic in dimension r there exists an element of $C_{r+1}(M_i\,;\,Z)$, which we call $D_r(t_i^r)$, such that

$$\partial_{r+1}D_r(t_i^r) = \zeta_r\, C_r(\tau)(t_i^r) - t_i^r - D_{r-1}\, \partial_r(t_i^r).$$

At this stage we have defined $D_r(t_i^r)$ for each elementary integral r-chain t_i^r of K' in such a way that if t_i^r is an element of a complex L' in the collection $\mathscr{L}$, then $D_r(t_i^r)$ is an element of $C_{r+1}(L'\,;\,Z)$. For each complex L' in $\mathscr{L}$ and for each coefficient group G, the homomorphism

$$D_r : C_r(L'\,;\,G) \to C_{r+1}(L'\,;\,G)$$

is defined by

$$D_r(\textstyle\sum g^i t_i^r) = \sum g^i D_r(t_i^r).$$

It is now clear that

$$\partial_{r+1}D_r(\textstyle\sum g^i t_i^r) + D_{r-1}\, \partial_r(\sum g^i t_i^r) = \zeta_r\, C_r(\tau)(\sum g^i t_i^r) - \sum g^i t_i^r.$$

In other words, the homomorphism D_q has the required property in dimensions greater than zero.

Finally, in order to complete the proof we must give an explicit definition of the homomorphism $D_0 : C_0(L'\,;\,G) \to C_1(L'\,:\,G)$. For this purpose, observe that each elementary 0-chain of L' is a vertex a of L' and there exists a unique simplex of K, denoted by $s(a)$, containing the vertex a. Let $M(a)$ indicate the first barycentric subdivision of the closure of $s(a)$. It follows from the definitions of ζ and τ that a and $\zeta_0\, C_0(\tau)(a)$ are vertices of $M(a)$. The complex $M(a)$ is connected, and therefore $\zeta_0\, C_0(\tau)(a) - a$ bounds a 1-chain c^1 of $M(a)$. For each vertex a of L', choose such a chain c^1 and set $D_0(a) = c^1$. This enables one to define the homomorphism $D_0 : C_0(L'\,;\,G) \to C_1(L'\,;\,G)$ by $D_0(\sum g^i\, a_i) = \sum g^i D_0(a_i)$. Since we have $\zeta_0\, C_0(\tau)(a) - a = \partial_1 D_0(a)$ for each vertex a of L', it follows that the same relation holds for arbitrary 0-chains of L'. That is, $\zeta_0\, C_0(\tau)(c^0) - c^0 = \partial_1 D_0(c^0)$ and this establishes the existence of the required homomorphism in dimension $q = 0$.

DEFINITION 26. For each simplicial complex K the chain transformation $\zeta : C(K;\,G) \to C(K';\,G)$ is called the subdivision chain transformation.

To summarize the developments of this section, we recall that if K' is the first barycentric subdivision of a complex K, then there is a simplicial approximation $\tau : K' \to K$ of the identity map. If L is a subcomplex of K, then L' is a subcomplex of K' and the pair (K', L') is called the first barycentric subdivision of the pair (K, L). The functor C assigns to each simplicial approximation of the identity map $\tau : (K', L') \to (K, L)$ a chain transformation $C(\tau) : C(K', L'; G) \to C(K, L; G)$ which is a chain homotopy inverse of the chain transformation $\zeta : C(K, L; G) \to C(K', L'; G)$. The homology functor H assigns to $C(K, L; G)$ and $C(K', L'; G)$ the graded groups $H(K, L; G)$ and $H(K', L'; G)$ and to ζ and $C(\tau)$ the homomorphisms $H(\zeta)$ and $H(\tau)$ which are usually abbreviated ζ_* and τ_*. Since ζ and $C(\tau)$ are chain homotopy equivalences, we have as special cases of Theorem 7 that ζ_* and τ_* are isomorphisms. The fact that $H(K, L; G)$ and $H(K', L'; G)$ are isomorphic is expressed by saying that the homology groups are invariant under barycentric subdivision. Corresponding to the sequence $(K^{(1)}, L^{(1)})$ $(K^{(2)}, L^{(2)})$, ... of successive barycentric subdivisions of a simplicial pair (K, L) there is a sequence of subdivision chain transformations

$$C(K, L; G) \to C(K^{(1)}, L^{(1)}; G) \to C(K^{(2)}, L^{(2)}; G) \to \ldots .$$

The composed transformation $C(K, L; G) \to C(K^{(n)}, L^{(n)}; G)$ is also called a subdivision transformation and is a chain homotopy inverse of $C(\tau)$ where $\tau : (K^{(n)}, L^{(n)}) \to (K, L)$ is any simplicial approximation of the identity.

EXERCISE 5

1. Show that a complex K is a cone complex if and only if K is the closed star of some vertex.

2. Show that the polytope of a cone complex is a contractible space.

3. Prove Theorem 25.

4. For each cone complex $p*K$ there are homomorphisms $D_q : C_q (K; G) \to C_{q+1}(p*K; G)$ given by $D_q(c) = p*c$. Use the results of Problem 7, Exercise 2 to show that these homomorphisms induce isomorphisms $\overline{D}_q : H_q(K; G) \to H_{q+1}(p*K, K; G)$.

5. Recall that for each coefficient group G there is a functor C which assigns to a complex K the nonnegative chain complex $C(K; G)$, sometimes called the chain complex of K over G. According to the

definition, $C_q(K; G) = 0$ for $q < 0$. The *augmented* chain complex of K over G is a chain complex $\tilde{C}(K; G)$ differing from $C(K; G)$ only in that $\tilde{C}_{-1}(K; G)$ is defined as the group G. Thus $\tilde{C}(K; G)$ is the sequence.

$$\cdots \xrightarrow{\tilde{\partial}_2} C_1(K; G) \xrightarrow{\tilde{\partial}_1} C_0(K; G) \xrightarrow{\tilde{\partial}_0} G \to 0 \cdots$$

For $q > 0$, $\tilde{\partial}_q$ is defined as the ordinary boundary homomorphism and $\tilde{\partial}_0$ is the Kronecker index homomorphism.

Prove that the augmented chain complex of a cone complex over any coefficient group is acyclic. Hint: Define a chain homotopy

$$D : \tilde{C}(p*K; G) \to \tilde{C}(p*K; G)$$

as follows. For $q \geqslant 0$,

$$D_q : C_q(p*K; G) \to C_{q+1}(p*K; G)$$

is given by

$$D_q(\langle a_0, a_1, \ldots, a_r \rangle) = \begin{cases} \langle p, a_0, a_1, \ldots, a_r \rangle & \text{if } p \notin \{a_0, a_1, \ldots, a_r\} \\ 0 & \text{if } p \in \{a_0, a_1, \ldots, a_r\} \end{cases}$$

Finally, the homomorphism $D_{-1} : G \to C_0(p*K; G)$ assigns to a group element g the chain gp.

6. Let $t^r = \langle p_0, p_1, \ldots, p_r \rangle$ be an oriented r-simplex of the first barycentric subdivision of an oriented r-simplex $s^r = \langle a_0, a_1, \ldots, a_r \rangle$ and let λ_j^i be the barycentric coordinates of p_i in terms of the a_j's. Show that t^r is oriented like s^r if and only if the determinant $|\lambda_j^i|$ is positive.

11. HOMOLOGY GROUPS OF POLYTOPE PAIRS

In Section 2 we considered the functor which assigned the graded group $H(K, L; G)$ to each simplicial pair (K, L). Now, having established the invariance of the homology groups of simplicial pairs under barycentric subdivision, we are ready to describe a covariant functor from the category of polytope pairs to the category of graded groups. To each polytope pair (X, A) this functor assigns a graded group $H(X, A; G)$ and assigns to each polytope map $f : (X, A) \to (Y, B)$ a homomorphism of degree zero $H(f) : H(X, A) \to H(Y, B)$. The symbol for the homomorphism $H(f)$ is usually abbreviated f_*.

The first step in the description of the new functor is to prove that if $(|K_1|, |L_1|)$ is homeomorphic to $(|K_2|, |L_2|)$, then $H(K_1, L_1; G)$ and $H(K_2, L_2; G)$ are isomorphic. This result is often expressed by saying that the simplicial homology groups are topologically invariant.

THEOREM 28. If $f: (|K_1|, |L_1|) \to (|K_2|, |L_2|)$ is a homeomorphism and if $\tau: (K_1, L_1) \to (K_2, L_2)$ is a simplicial approximation of f, then for each r, $\tau_*: H_r(K_1, L_1; G) \to H_r(K_2, L_2; G)$ is an isomorphism.

Proof: The hypothesis that τ is a simplicial approximation of f includes the assumption that K_1 is star related to K_2 with respect to f. Choose a subdivision K_2' of K_2 such that K_2' is star related to K_1 with respect to f^{-1} and choose a subdivision K_1' of K_1 which is star related to K_2' with respect to f. Then we have the following sequence of simplicial maps.

$$(K_1', L_1') \xrightarrow{\tau^3} (K_2', L_2') \xrightarrow{\tau^2} (K_1, L_1) \xrightarrow{\tau^1} (K_2, L_2)$$

where τ^3, τ^2, and τ^1 are simplicial approximations of f, f^{-1}, and f. There is also the corresponding sequence of homology groups and induced homomorphisms for each dimension:

$$H_r(K_1', L_1'; G) \xrightarrow{\tau_*^3} H_r(K_2', L_2'; G) \xrightarrow{\tau_*^2} H_r(K_1, L_1; G) \xrightarrow{\tau_*^1} H_r(K_2, L_2; G).$$

Since ff^{-1} and $f^{-1}f$ are identity maps with simplicial approximations $\tau^2\tau^3$ and $\tau^1\tau^2$, by the results of Section 10 $\tau_*^2\tau_*^3$ and $\tau_*^1\tau_*^2$ are isomorphisms. An easy algebraic argument now shows that τ_*^1 is an isomorphism, and the proof is complete.

The topological invariance of the simplicial homology groups as given in the next theorem is an immediate consequence of Theorem 28.

THEOREM 29. Let $f: (|K_1|, |L_1|) \to (|K_2|, |L_2|)$ be a homeomorphism and let $K_1^{(m)}$ be a barycentric subdivision of K_1 such that $K_1^{(m)}$ is star related to K_2 with respect to the map f. Also let $\tau: (K_1^{(m)}, L_1^{(m)}) \to (K_2, L_2)$ be a simplicial approximation of f and let $\zeta_*: H_r(K_1, L_1) \to H_r(K_1^{(m)}, L_1^{(m)})$ be the subdivision homomorphism. Then the composed homomorphism

$$\tau_* \zeta_*: H_r(K_1, L_1; G) \to H_r(K_2, L_2; G)$$

is an isomorphism.

Proof: The composition of the isomorphisms ζ_* and τ_* is an isomorphism.

The new homology functor H (to be defined later) actually has as its domain a category somewhat larger than the category of polytopes as previously defined. The corresponding extension of the concept of a polytope is given next.

DEFINITION 27. A *topological polytope* is a topological space X homeomorphic to the space $|K|$ of some complex. A topological polytope pair is a topological pair (X, A) homeomorphic to a pair $(|K|, |L|)$ where (K, L) is a simplicial pair. A triangulation of a topological polytope pair (X, A) is a triple (K, L, f) where (K, L) is a simplicial pair and $f : (|K|, |L|) \rightarrow (X, A)$ is a homeomorphism.

In the future, the adjective "topological" will be dropped and "polytope" will mean "topological polytope." The term rectilinear polytope is sometimes used to denote a polytope in the earlier sense.

Suppose, next, that (K_1, L_1, f) and (K_2, L_2, g) are triangulations of a polytope pair (X, A). There exists a barycentric subdivision K_1' of K_1 which is star related to K_2 with respect to the composed map

$$g^{-1}f : (|K_1'|, |L_1'|) \rightarrow (|K_2|, |L_2|).$$

Let

$$\zeta_* : H_r(K_1, L_1; G) \rightarrow H_r(K_1', L_1'; G)$$

be the subdivision homomorphism and let

$$\tau : (K_1', L_1') \rightarrow (K_2, L_2)$$

be a simplicial approximation of the map $g^{-1}f$. Then

$$\tau_* \zeta_* : H_r(K_1, L_1; G) \rightarrow H_r(K_2, L_2; G)$$

is an isomorphism and establishes a definite one-to-one correspondence between the elements of $H_r(K_1, L_1; G)$ and those of $H_r(K_2, L_2; G)$. The idea now is to define the r-dimensional homology group $H_r(X, A; G)$ of the polytope pair by saying that elements h_1 of $H_r(K_1, L_1; G)$ and h_2 of $H_r(K_2, L_2; G)$ represent the same element of $H_r(X, A; G)$ provided

$\tau_* \zeta_*(h_1) = h_2$. Before this can be done, however, two points must be cleared up.

In the first place, two choices were made in the construction of the homomorphism $\tau_* \zeta_*$, namely the choice of the subdivision K_1' and that of the simplicial map τ. It must be shown that the final homomorphism $\tau_* \zeta_*$ does not depend upon these choices. Also in order to show that the provisional definition suggested above is meaningful, one must prove that the relation given by $\tau_* \zeta_*(h_1) = h_2$ is an equivalence relation. These questions are covered in the next two theorems.

THEOREM 30. If $f : (|K_1|, |L_1|) \to (|K_2|, |L_2|)$ is a map and K_1' is a barycentric subdivision of K_1 star related to K_2 with respect to the map f, and $\tau : (K_1', L_1') \to (K_2, L_2)$ is a simplicial approximation of f, then the homomorphism

$$\tau_* \zeta_* : H_r(K_1, L_1; G) \to H_r(K_2, L_2; G)$$

is independent of K_1' and τ.

Proof: First consider the case where K_1 is star related to K_2 with respect to f. Suppose that K_1' is a subdivision of K_1 and that $\tau^1 : (K_1, L_1) \to (K_2, L_2)$ and $\tau^2 : (K_1', L_1') \to (K_2, L_2)$ are simplicial approximations of f. It will be shown that $\tau^1_* = \tau^2_* \zeta_*$ where $\zeta_* : H_r(K_1, L_1; G) \to H_r(K_1', L_1'; G)$ is the subdivision homomorphism. For this purpose, let $\sigma : (K_1', L_1') \to (K_1, L_1)$ be a simplicial approximation of the identity. By Theorem 24, $\sigma_* \zeta_*$ is the identity mapping of $H(K_1, L_1; G)$. In addition, $\tau^1 \sigma$ and τ^2 are contiguous since each is a simplicial approximation of f. Consequently $\tau^2_* \zeta_* = (\tau^1 \sigma)_* \zeta_* = \tau^1_*(\sigma_* \zeta_*) = \tau^1_*$. This completes the proof for the special case under consideration.

To make the proof for the general case consider the following diagram

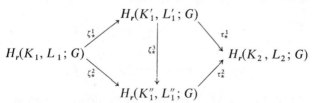

Here it is assumed that K_1' and K_1'' are barycentric subdivisions of K_1 with K_1'' of higher order than K_1'. That is, K_1'' is a subdivision of K_1'. In the diagram, the triangle on the left is commutative by definition and the triangle

on the right is commutative by the special case already proved. It follows that $\tau_*^1 \zeta_*^1 = \tau_*^2 \zeta_*^2$.

DEFINITION 28. Let (K_1, L_1, f) and (K_2, L_2, g) be triangulations of a polytope pair (X, A). Let $\tau : (K_1', L_1') \to (K_2, L_2)$ be a simplicial approximation of $g^{-1}f$ and let

$$\tau_* \zeta_* : H_r(K_1, L_1; G) \to H_r(K_2, L_2; G)$$

be the homomorphism of Theorem 30. Then an element h of $H_r(K_1, L_1; G)$ is said to be equivalent to an element h' of $H_r(K_2, L_2; G)$ if $h' = \tau_* \zeta_*(h)$. If h is equivalent to h' we write $h \sim h'$.

THEOREM 31. Let h_1, h_2, h_3 be elements of $H_r(K_1, L_1; G)$, $H_r(K_2, L_2; G)$, and $H_r(K_3, L_3; G)$ where (K_1, L_1, f_1), (K_2, L_2, f_2), and (K_3, L_3, f_3) are triangulations of a polytope pair (X, A). Then

(a) $h_1 \sim h_1$,

(b) $h_1 \sim h_2$ implies $h_2 \sim h_1$,

(c) $h_1 \sim h_2$ and $h_2 \sim h_3$ implies $h_1 \sim h_3$.

Proof: The proof of part (b) only will be given. The others, being easier, will be left to the reader.

Suppose then that h_1 and h_2 are as in the statement of the theorem, and let us first select a subdivision K_2' of K_2 star related to K_1 with respect to the composed map $f_1^{-1}f_2$ and then a subdivision K_1' of K_1 star related to K_2' with respect to $f_2^{-1}f_1$. It is clear that K_1' is star related to K_2 with respect to $f_2^{-1}f_1$ and thus the next diagram follows.

$$
\begin{array}{ccc}
H_r(K_1, L_1; G) & \xleftarrow{\ \rho_* \ } & H_r(K_2', L_2'; G) \\
{\scriptstyle \zeta_*^1} \downarrow & {\scriptstyle \sigma_*} \nearrow & \uparrow {\scriptstyle \zeta_*^2} \\
H_r(K_1', L_1'; G) & \xrightarrow{\ \tau_* \ } & H_r(K_2, L_2; G)
\end{array}
$$

In this diagram each ζ_*^i represents a subdivision homomorphism; ρ_* and σ_* are induced by simplicial approximations of the maps $f_1^{-1}f_2$ and $f_2^{-1}f_1$ respectively. The homomorphism τ_* is defined as follows. Let $\eta : K_2' \to K_2$ be a simplicial approximation of the identity so that η_* is the inverse of ζ_*^2. The map τ is defined as the composed map $\eta\sigma$ so that τ is a simplicial approximation of $f_2^{-1}f_1$ and $\tau_* = \eta_*\sigma_*$. This last equation can be written $\zeta_*^2\tau_* = \sigma_*$, which means that the triangle occupying the lower right hand half of the diagram is commutative. Regarding the triangle in the upper left of the diagram, we see that $\rho\sigma$ is a simplicial approximation of the identity so that $\rho_*\sigma_*\zeta_*^1 = $ identity.

After these preliminaries, the proof of part (b) is purely mechanical. By definition, $h_1 \sim h_2$ implies that $\tau_*\zeta_*^1(h_1) = h_2$. To prove $h_2 \sim h_1$ it will be sufficient to show that $\rho_*\zeta_*^2(h_2) = h_1$. Then

$$\rho_*\zeta_*^2(h_2) = \rho_*\zeta_*^2\tau_*\zeta_*^1(h_1) = \rho_*\sigma_*\zeta_*^1(h_1) = h_1.$$

Having proved Theorems 30 and 31, we are in a position to describe the object function of a functor from the category of polytope pairs to the category of graded groups. This functor H will assign to each polytope pair (X, A) a graded group $H(X, A; G) = \{H_r(X, A; G)\}$. One usually thinks intuitively of the homology group $H_r(X, A; G)$ as being identical with the group $H_r(K, L; G)$ where (K, L, f) is any triangulation of (X, A). Theorems 30 and 31 are exactly what is needed to make this idea workable. An element of the group $H_r(X, A; G)$ is actually an equivalence class of elements under the relation given in Definition 28. If h is an element of $H_r(K, L; G)$ where (K, L, f) is a triangulation of (X, A), then the equivalence class containing h is denoted by $\{h\}$. As a matter of actual practice, when one works with the homology group $H_r(X, A; G)$ of a polytope pair he usually chooses a convenient triangulation (K, L, f) and works with the group $H_r(K, L; G)$. This is justified, of course, by the fact that each element of $H_r(X, A; G)$ has a unique representative in the group $H_r(K, L; G)$. This fact is also used in the formal definition of the group operation in $H_r(X, A; G)$. The rule for addition is $\{h_1\} + \{h_2\} = \{h_1 + h_2\}$ where h_1 and h_2 are both elements of $H_r(K, L; G)$ for some triangulation. These remarks are summarized in the next definition.

DEFINITION 29. The group whose underlying set is the set of equivalence classes under the relation given in Definition 28 and whose operation is the addition defined above is denoted by the symbol $H_r(X, A; G)$ and is called the r-dimensional homology group of (X, A) with coefficients in G. The graded homology group of the polytope pair (X, A) is the graded group $H(X, A; G) = \{H_r(X, A; G)\}$.

In order to complete the definition of the homology functor H on the category of polytope pairs, all that remains is to describe the manner in which this functor assigns to each polytope map $f : (X, A) \to (Y, B)$ an induced homomorphism $f_* : H_r(X, A; G) \to H_r(Y, B; G)$. The idea is to choose a triangulation (K_1, L_1, g_1) of (X, A) and (K_2, L_2, g_2) of (Y, B) such that K_1 is star related to K_2 with respect to the map $g_2^{-1}fg_1$ and a simplicial approximation $\tau : (K_1, L_1) \to (K_2, L_2)$ of $g_2^{-1}fg_1$, and to define for each $h \in H_r(K_1, L_1; G)$, $f_*\{h\} = \{\tau_*(h)\}$. Of course, it must be shown that the image of an element of $H_r(X, A; G)$ is independent of the particular representative chosen. This is done in the next theorem.

We will suppose that $f : (X, A) \to (Y, B)$ is a polytope map, that (K_1, L_1, h_1) and (K_2, L_2, h_2) are triangulations of (X, A), and that (M_1, N_1, g_1) and (M_2, N_2, g_2) are triangulations of (Y, B). There exist subdivisions K_1', K_2', and M_1' of K_1, K_2, and M_1 such that M_1' is star related to M_2 with respect to $g_2^{-1}g_1$, K_2' is star related to M_2 with respect to $g_2^{-1}fh_2$, K_1' is star related to M_1' and K_2' with respect to $g_1^{-1}fh_1$ and $h_2^{-1}h_1$. In the following diagram the τ_*^i are induced by simplicial approximations of these maps and the ζ_*^i are subdivision homomorphisms.

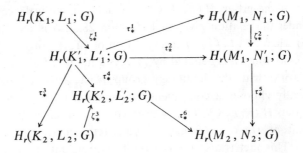

THEOREM 32. With reference to the diagram above,

$$\tau_*^5 \zeta_*^2 \tau_*^1 = \tau_*^6 \zeta_*^3 \tau_*^3.$$

Proof: It is easy to establish commutativity in each of the two triangles and the quadrilateral of the diagram. For example, $(\zeta_*^2)^{-1}$ is a simplicial approximation of the identity so that τ_*^1 and $(\zeta_*^2)^{-1}\tau_*^2$ are each induced by simplicial approximations of $g_1^{-1}fh_1$. Consequently, $\tau_*^1 = (\zeta_*^2)^{-1}\tau_*^2$ and this implies that $\zeta_*^2\tau_*^1 = \tau_*^2$. Likewise, $\tau^5\tau^2$ and $\tau^6\tau^4$ are simplicial approximations of $g_2^{-1}fh_1$ and this implies commutativity for the quadrilateral.

The proof of the theorem follows immediately from the commutativity of the diagram.

Verification of conditions (2) and (3) in the definition of a covariant functor (Definition 3) is done in the following theorem. The proof is left as an exercise.

THEOREM 33. If $f : (X, A) \to (Y, B)$ and $g : (Y, B) \to (Z, C)$ are polytope maps, then $g_* f_* = (gf)_*$. If f is the identity map, then f_* is the identity homomorphism.

COROLLARY. If $f : (X, A) \to (Y, B)$ is a homeomorphism, then $f_* : H_r(X, A; G) \to H_r(Y, B; G)$ is an isomorphism.

12. HOMOTOPY INVARIANCE OF HOMOLOGY GROUPS

In the present chapter the discussion has been centered around four categories. The objects in the categories $\mathscr{P}$, $\mathscr{S}$, $\mathscr{C}$, and $\mathscr{H}$ are respectively polytope pairs, simplicial pairs, chain complexes, and finally, graded groups. Three functors $|\ |$, C, and H are illustrated in the diagram

$$
\begin{array}{ccc}
\mathscr{P} & \cdots\!\!\longrightarrow & \mathscr{H} \\
{\scriptstyle|\ |}\Big\uparrow & & \Big\uparrow{\scriptstyle H} \\
\mathscr{S} & \xrightarrow{\ C\ } & \mathscr{C}
\end{array}
$$

The broken arrow $\mathscr{P} \cdots\!\!\longrightarrow \mathscr{H}$ indicates the functor of the preceding section which assigns to each polytope pair (X, A) the graded homology group $H(X, A; G)$.

In each of the categories $\mathscr{P}$, $\mathscr{S}$, and $\mathscr{C}$ there is a morphism equivalence relation. These are the homotopy relation, the contiguity relation, and the chain homotopy relation. Note that the phrase "the contiguity relation" is an abbreviation for "the relation of being in the same contiguity class." It will be convenient to consider the morphism equivalence relation of equality in the category $\mathscr{H}$ so that we have a morphism equivalence relation in each of the categories $\mathscr{P}$, $\mathscr{S}$, $\mathscr{C}$, and $\mathscr{H}$. Theorems 11, 13, and 14 can be summarized by the statement that the functors $|\ |$, C, and H respect these morphism equivalence relations. To round out the picture, we shall prove that if f_*, g_* : $H(X, A; G) \rightarrow H(Y, B; G)$ are homomorphisms assigned by the homology functor $\mathscr{P} \longrightarrow \mathscr{H}$ to homotopic maps $f, g : (X, A) \rightarrow (Y, B)$, then $f_* = g_*$. The proof will use the following lemma.

LEMMA 6. For each polytope pair (Y, B), there exists a positive number ε such that if f, $g : (X, A) \rightarrow (Y, B)$ are polytope maps satisfying the condition max $d(f(x), g(x)) < \varepsilon$, then $f_* = g_*$.

Proof: Let (K_2, L_2, h_2) be a triangulation of the pair (Y, B). Let $\mathscr{V}$ be the open covering of K_2 consisting of the stars of the vertices of K_2 and let 3ε be a Lebesgue number of the open covering $h_2(\mathscr{V})$ of Y.

Now suppose that f and g are maps of a pair (X, A) into (Y, B) such that max $d(f(x), g(x)) < \varepsilon$. Next choose a triangulation (K_1, L_1, h_1) of (X, A) with mesh so small that for each vertex v of K_1 the diameter of each of the sets $fh_1(\text{star}(v))$ and $gh_1(\text{star}(v))$ is less than ε. It follows that the set $\{fh_1(\text{star}(v)) \cup gh_1(\text{star}(v))\}$ has diameter less than 3ε and therefore is contained in one of the sets of the covering $h_2(\mathscr{V})$ of Y. This in turn means that there exists a vertex w of K_2 such that $h_2^{-1}fh_1$ and $h_2^{-1}gh_1$ both map the star of v into the star of w. It is possible to choose such a vertex w for each vertex v of K_1 in such a way that if v is in L_1, then w is in L_2. The simplicial mapping $\tau : (K_1, L_1) \rightarrow (K_2, L_2)$ so determined is a simplicial approximation of both $h_2^{-1}fh_1$ and $h_2^{-1}gh_1$. Finally, let the element h of $H_r(K_1, L_1; G)$ represent the element $\{h\}$ of $H_r(X, A; G)$. Then, by definition, $f_*\{h\} = \{\tau_*(h)\} = g_*\{h\}$. This completes the proof of the lemma.

THEOREM 34. If $f, g : (X, A) \rightarrow (Y, B)$ are homotopic polytope maps, then the induced homomorphisms f_* and g_* are identical.

Proof: Choose a homotopy $H : f \simeq g$ from f to g. Let ε be a positive number related to (Y, B) as in the lemma. A consequence of the uniform continuity of the function H is that there exists a positive number δ such that for each pair of elements s and t of I satisfying $|s - t| < \delta$, it is true that max $d(H(x, t), H(x, s)) < \varepsilon$. Next choose a finite sequence of numbers $t_0, t_1, \ldots, t_p$ in I such that $t_0 = 0$, $t_p = 1$, and $|t_{i+1} - t_i| < \delta$ for $i = 0, 1, \ldots, p - 1$. Also, for each $i = 0, 1, \ldots, p$, let $H^i : (X, A) \rightarrow (Y, B)$ be the map given by $H^i(x) = H(x, t_i)$. Then for each $i < p$, $H_*^i = H_*^{i+1}$; thus $f_* = H_*^0 = H_*^p = g_*$ and this concludes the proof.

Having proved Theorem 34, a special case of Theorem 7 is the result that if polytope pairs (X, A) and (Y, B) have the same homotopy type, then the graded homology groups $H(X, A; G)$ and $H(Y, B; G)$ are isomorphic. This is often expressed by saying that the homology groups are homotopy invariant.

EXERCISE 6

1. Prove Theorem 31, (a) and (c).

2. Prove that there is associated with each polytope Y a positive number ε such that if f, $g : X \to Y$ are polytope maps satisfying max $d(f(x), g(x)) < \varepsilon$, then $f \simeq g$. Hint: Examine the proof of Lemma 5.

3. Use the results of Problem 4, Exercise 5, Chapter I and the fact that a 2-sphere is homeomorphic to the boundary of a 3-simplex to prove that a 2-sphere is not contractible.

CHAPTER III

ELEMENTARY APPLICATIONS

Applications of homology theory depend on precise information about the nature of groups and homomorphisms assigned by the homology functor H to polytopes and mappings. In this introductory section, several items basic to the applications are developed and recorded.

One specific piece of information from Theorem 21 of Chapter I is that the zero-dimensional group $H_0(X; G)$ of a connected polytope X is isomorphic to the coefficient group G. Additional information about the zero-dimensional groups of a connected polytope is given in the next theorem.

THEOREM 1. Let $f: X \to X$ be any map of a connected polytope X. Then the induced homomorphism $f_*: H_0(X; G) \to H_0(X; G)$ in dimension zero is the identity homomorphism.

Proof: Let (K, g) be a triangulation of X and let K' be a sub-division of K star related to K with respect to $g^{-1}fg$. The set $\{a_i\}$ of vertices of K is a basis for $C_0(K; G) = Z_0(K; G)$. By hypothesis of connectedness, if a_i and a_j are vertices of K, then $a_i - a_j$ is a bounding 0-chain so that $\Theta(a_i) = \Theta(a_j)$ where $\Theta: Z_0(K; G) \to H_0(K; G)$ is the natural homomor-phism. If h is any element of $H_0(K; G)$, then $h = \Theta(c^0) = \Theta(\sum g^i a_i) = \sum g^i \Theta(a_i) = (\sum g^i)\Theta(a_0)$. This means that the single element $\Theta(a_0)$ is a basis of $H_0(K; G)$. Now let $\zeta: C_0(K; G) \to C_0(K'; G)$ be the subdivision homomorphism and let $\tau: K' \to K$ be a simplicial approximation of $g^{-1}fg$. Then $\tau_\#(a_0) = a_k$ for some k and consequently $f_*\Theta(a_0) = \Theta(\tau_\# \zeta(a_0)) = \Theta(a_k) = \Theta(a_0)$. This implies $f_* =$ identity and completes the proof.

If X is a polytope and, for some integer r, $H_r(X; G) = 0$ for each coefficient group G, then X is said to be "homologically trivial" in di-mension r. We have seen that if K is a nonnull complex and G is a non-trivial coefficient group, then $H_0(K; G) \neq 0$. On the other hand, if K is connected, then $\tilde{H}_0(K; G) = 0$ for every coefficient group. Because of these facts, it is customary to call a polytope homologically trivial or "acyclic" provided that for every coefficient group G, $H_r(X; G) = 0$ for $r > 0$ and $\tilde{H}_0(X; G) = 0$.

Among the simplest and most useful homologically nontrivial polytopes are the n-spheres, while the n-cells are all acyclic. Some of the properties of these polytopes will be worked out with future applications in mind.

DEFINITION 1. The n-dimensional sphere S^n and the $(n + 1)$-dimensional cell E^{n+1} are the subspaces of R^{n+1} given by

$$S^n = \{(x^1, x^2, \ldots, x^{n+1}) \in R^{n+1} : \sum (x^i)^2 = 1\}$$
$$E^{n+1} = \{(x^1, x^2, \ldots, x^{n+1}) \in R^{n+1} : \sum (x^i)^2 \leq 1\}.$$

It is easy to seee that S^n is the point set boundary of E^{n+1} in R^{n+1} and it will be shown that (E^{n+1}, S^n) is a polytope pair; that is, there is a simplicial pair (K, L) such that $(|K|, |L|)$ is homeomorphic to (E^{n+1}, S^n).

THEOREM 2. Let K be the combinatorial closure of an $(n + 1)$-simplex s^{n+1} and let L be the combinatorial boundary of s^{n+1}. Then $(|K|, |L|)$ is homeomorphic to (E^{n+1}, S^n).

Proof: To start the proof, let s^{n+1} be an $(n + 1)$-simplex contained in R^{n+1} and let p be its centroid. Select a positive number δ such that the set $X = \{x \in R^{n+1} : d(x, p) \leqslant \delta\}$ is contained in s^{n+1}. Let

$$A = \{x \in R^{n+1} : d(x, p) = \delta\}.$$

It is clear that (X, A) is homeomorphic to (E^{n+1}, S^n) and it will be shown that (X, A) is homeomorphic to $(|K|, |L|)$. The required bijective mapping between X and $|K|$ is established as follows. For each point $x \neq p$ of X, the line $\pi(x, p)$ intersects A and $|L|$ in unique points designated by $g(x)$ and $h(x)$. Now $x = t(x)p + (1 - t(x))g(x)$ for some $t(x)$, $0 \leqslant t(x) \leqslant 1$. Make the definition $f(x) = t(x)p + (1 - t(x))h(x)$, and f becomes a bijective function from (X, A) to $(|K|, |L|)$. The continuity oj the function f is proved by an elementary argument involving the continuity of barycentric coordinates and the distance function.

In accordance with the practice of identifying homeomorphic spaces, it is customary to call any space homeomorphic to S^n an *n*-sphere and to call any space homeomorphic to E^n an *n*-cell. The basic homological facts about S^n and E^n are set out in the next theorem.

THEOREM 3. $H_r(S^n, G)$ is isomorphic to G for $r = 0$ or n.

$H_r(S^n, G) = 0$ for r not equal to 0 or n.

$H_0(E^n, G)$ is isomorphic to G.

$H_r(E^n, G) = 0$ for $r > 0$.

Proof: To compute the homology groups of S^n, it will suffice to compute the groups of any convenient triangulating complex. The complex L described above as the combinatorial boundary of s^{n+1} is well suited to this task. Since L has no $(n + 1)$-simplexes, we have $H_n(L, G) \approx Z_n(L, G)$. An *n*-chain of L over G has the form $c^n = \sum g^i s_i^n$ where $\{s_i^n\}$ is the set of *n*-simplexes of L. Such a chain will be a cycle if and only if all the coefficients g_i are equal. To see that this is the case, compute the boundary of the chain $c^n = \sum g^i s_i^n$. Assume that s^{n+1} is oriented and we may orient L so that each s_i^n receives the orientation it inherits from s^{n+1}. Consider a fixed $(n-1)$-simplex t_k^{n-1} of L. This simplex t_k^{n-1} is incident to exactly two n-simplexes s_p^n and s_q^n. By Theorem 13 of Chapter I, $[s_p^n : t_k^{n-1}] = -[s_q^n : t_k^{n-1}]$. Now let g^k be the coefficient of t_k^{n-1} in the chain $\partial(\sum g^i s_i^n)$ and it follows that $g^k = \pm(g^p - g^q)$. This means that $c^n = \sum g^i s_i^n$ is a cycle if and only if for each i and j, $g^i = g^j$. Thus we have shown that each cycle of $Z_n(L)$ is of the form $c^n = \sum gs_i^n$. The mapping $v : Z_n(L) \to G$ given by $v(\sum gs_i^n) = g$ is an isomorphism, and $H_n(S^n, G) \approx Z_n(L, G) \approx G$.

Also, since L is connected, $H_0(S^n, G) \approx H_0(L, G) \approx G$.

For $r > n$, $H_r(L, G) = 0$ by definition.

For the cases $0 < r < n$, let q be a vertex of s^{n+1} and define $D_r : C_r(L, G) \to C_{r+1}(L, G)$ by

$$
D_r\langle a_0, \ldots, a_r\rangle = \begin{cases} \langle q, a_0, \ldots, a_r\rangle & \text{if } q \text{ is not a vertex of } \langle a_0, \ldots, a_r\rangle \\ 0 & \text{if } q \text{ is a vertex of } \langle a_0, \ldots, a_r\rangle \end{cases}
$$

Then for each $c^r \in C_r(L)$, $c^r = \partial_{r+1} D_r(c^r) + D_{r-1}\partial_r(c^r)$, and it follows that $H_r(L, G) = 0$.

The statements regarding $H_r(E^n, G)$ are easy consequences of the following lemma.

LEMMA 1. A contractible polytope is acyclic.

Proof of Lemma 1: It is very easy to see that a contractible polytope X has the same homotopy type as a space P consisting of a single point. Hence the chain-complexes $C(X, G)$ and $C(P, G)$ are chain-homotopic equivalent and the graded homology groups $H(X, G)$ and $H(P, G)$ are isomorphic. Also, $H_r(P, G) = 0$ for $r > 0$ since the complex P has no simplexes of positive dimension. Finally, $\tilde{H}_0(P, G) = 0$ since P is connected. This completes the proof of the lemma.

To prove that E^n is contractible, it is sufficient to observe that the map $H : E^n \times I \to E^n$ given by $H(x, t) = (1 - t)x$ is a homotopy from the identity map of E^n to the map which carries all of E^n into the origin.

1. HOPF'S THEOREM

In this section we shall prove a theorem of H. Hopf which will lead to our first applications of homology theory. These applications will be good examples of the techniques of algebraic topology.

In the constructions to follow, the additive group of a field F will be used exclusively as coefficient group. Consequently, we shall write $C_r(K), Z_r(K), H_r(K), \ldots$ for $C_r(K, F), Z_r(K, F), H_r(K, F), \ldots$.

The fact that the set F is a field permits the definition of a "scalar multiplication" in the chain groups $C_r(K)$ and then $C_r(K)$ is a vector space over F. This scalar multiplication is given in the next definition.

DEFINITION 2. Let K be a complex. For each $x \in F$ and for each $c^r = \sum y^i s_i^r \in C_r(K)$, define $xc^r \in C_r(K)$ by

$$xc^r = x(\sum y^i s_i^r) = \sum (xy^i)s_i^r.$$

THEOREM 4. Under the scalar multiplication of Definition 2, $C_r(K)$ is a vector space over F. The boundary homomorphism $\partial_r : C_r(K) \to C_{r-1}(K)$ is a linear transformation. Also $Z_r(K)$, $B_r(K)$, and $H_r(K)$ are vector spaces over F. For each simplicial map $\tau : K \to L$, the induced homomorphisms $C_r(\tau) : C_r(K) \to C_r(L)$ and $\tau_* : H_r(K) \to H_r(L)$ are linear transformations.

The proof of Theorem 4 is completely routine. $C_r(K)$ is actually a finite-dimensional vector space since the set of oriented r-simplexes is a basis. The kernel and image of $\partial : C_r(K) \to C_{r-1}(K)$ are $Z_r(K)$ and $B_{r-1}(K)$ respectively. Finally, $H_r(K)$ is the quotient space $Z_r(K)/B_r(K)$.

It will be necessary to recall several items from the theory of vector spaces for use here. The *trace* of a square matrix $A = (a_{ij})$, written $\mathrm{tr}(A)$, is defined as the sum of the diagonal elements of A. Thus $\mathrm{tr}(A) = \sum a_{ii}$. The trace of A is also the sum of the characteristic roots of A. Accordingly, if A, B, and P are matrices with P nonsingular and $A = PBP^{-1}$, then $\mathrm{tr}(A =) \mathrm{tr}(B)$. Therefore, if $T : V \to V$ is a linear transformation, and if A and B are matrices representing T with respect to certain bases of V, then there exists a nonsingular matrix P such that $A = PBP^{-1}$ and we have $\mathrm{tr}(A) = \mathrm{tr}(B)$. Consequently, the trace of the transformation T can be defined as the trace of any matrix representing T.

If $T : V \to V$ is a linear transformation and W is a T-invariant subspace of V (this means that $T(W) \subset W$), then we may consider the transformation obtained by restricting T to the space W. The trace of T restricted to W is denoted by $\mathrm{tr}(T, W)$. Suppose next that $\Theta : V \to V_0$ is a surjective linear transformation, that $W = \text{kernel}(\Theta)$, that T is a linear transformation of V into V, and that W is T-invariant. Then by the induced homomorphism theorem, there exists a linear transformation $\overline{T}: V_0 \to V_0$ such that $\overline{T}\Theta = \Theta T$.

$$
\begin{array}{ccc}
V_0 & \xrightarrow{\ T\ } & V_0 \\
{\scriptstyle \Theta}\uparrow & & \uparrow{\scriptstyle \Theta} \\
V & \xrightarrow{\ T\ } & V
\end{array}
$$

THEOREM 5. In the notation of the preceding paragraph,

$$\text{tr}(T, V) = \text{tr}(\overline{T}, V_0) + \text{tr}(T, W).$$

Proof: Select a basis $\{\alpha_1, \alpha_2, \ldots, \alpha_k\}$ of W and then a set $\{\beta_1, \ldots, \beta_n\}$ such that $\{\alpha_1, \ldots, \alpha_k, \beta_1, \ldots, \beta_n\}$ is a basis of V. For each β_i, define $\gamma_i = \Theta(\beta_i)$ and show that $\{\gamma_1, \ldots, \gamma_n\}$ is a basis of V_0. Since W is T-invariant, we have for each α_i, $T(\alpha_i) = \sum a_i^j \alpha_j$, and for each β_i $T(\beta_i) = \sum c_i^j \alpha_j + \sum b_i^j \beta_j$. This means that the matrix representing $T: V \to V$ with respect to the chosen basis has the form

$$M = \left(\begin{array}{c:c} A & C \\ \hdashline 0 & B \end{array}\right)$$

where $A = (a_i^j)$ and $B = (b_i^j)$. It is a matter of definition that the matrix A represents the transformation $T: W \to W$ and to complete the proof it will be shown that B represents the transformation $\overline{T}: V_0 \to V_0$ with respect to the basis $\{\gamma_1, \ldots, \gamma_n\}$. Observe that $\overline{T}(\gamma_i) = \overline{T}\Theta(\beta_i) = \Theta T(\beta_i) = \Theta(\sum b_i^j \beta_j) = \sum b_i^j \Theta(\beta_j) = \sum b_i^j \gamma_j$ and the conclusion follows. We now have that $\text{tr}(T, V) = \text{tr}(M) = \text{tr}(A) + \text{tr}(B) = \text{tr}(T, W) + \text{tr}(\overline{T}, V_0)$ and the proof is complete.

Next let K be a complex and $\eta: C(K) \to C(K)$ a chain transformation such that for each r, $\eta_r: C_r(K) \to C_r(K)$ is a linear transformation. Such a chain transformation will be called a linear chain transformation. Since $Z_r(K)$ and $B_r(K)$ are η-invariant, we have in each dimension r the numbers $\text{tr}(\eta, C_r(K))$, $\text{tr}(\eta, Z_r(K))$, $\text{tr}(\eta, B_r(K))$, and $\text{tr}(\eta_*, H_r(K))$. Note that the subscript r has been omitted from the symbol η_r in this notation.

THEOREM 6. Let K be a complex and let $\eta: C(K) \to C(K)$ be a linear chain transformation. Then for each dimension r, $\text{tr}(\eta, C_r(K)) = \text{tr}(\eta_*, H_r(K)) + \text{tr}(\eta, B_r(K)) + \text{tr}(\eta, B_{r-1}(K))$.

Proof: The homomorphism $\delta_r : C_r(K) \to B_{r-1}(K)$ is surjective with kernel $Z_r(K)$ so that by Theorem 5

$$\mathrm{tr}(\eta, C_r(K)) = \mathrm{tr}(\eta, B_{r-1}(K)) + \mathrm{tr}(\eta, Z_r(K)).$$

In like manner, the natural homomorphism $\Theta : Z_r(K) \to H_r(K)$ is surjective and has kernel $B_r(K)$ so that, again by Theorem 5,

$$\mathrm{tr}(\eta, Z_r(K)) = \mathrm{tr}(\eta_*, H_r(K)) + \mathrm{tr}(\eta, B_r(K)).$$

The conclusion of the theorem is obtained by eliminating $\mathrm{tr}(\eta, Z_r(K))$ from the last two equations.

If $f: X \to X$ is a polytope map, then the groups $H_r(X)$ and the homomorphisms $f_* : H_r(X) \to H_r(X)$ are defined in a way that is independent of any particular triangulation of X. On the other hand, if there exists a triangulation (K, g) of X such that $\dim(K) = n$, then $H_r(X) = 0$ for r greater than n. Also $H_r(X)$ is a vector space isomorphic to $H_r(K)$ and if K' is a subdivision of K, $\tau : K' \to K$ is a simplicial approximation of $g^{-1}fg$, and $\zeta : C(K) \to C(K')$ is the subdivision chain transformation, then $\mathrm{tr}(f_*, H_r(X)) = \mathrm{tr}(\tau_* \zeta_*, H_r(K))$. The next theorem will treat the "alternating" sum $\sum(-1)^r \mathrm{tr}(f_*, H_r(X))$. This sum exists since there are only a finite number of nonzero terms.

THEOREM 7. (Hopf, 1928). Let $f: X \to X$ be a polytope map, (K, g) a triangulation of X, K' a subdivision of K, $\tau : K' \to K$ a simplicial approximation of $g^{-1}fg$, and $\zeta : C(K) \to C(K')$ the subdivision chain transformation. Then $\sum(-1)^r \mathrm{tr}(\tau_\# \zeta, C_r(K)) = \sum(-1)^r \mathrm{tr}(f_*, H_r(X))$.

Proof: From Theorem 6 we have

$$\mathrm{tr}(\tau_\# \zeta, C_r(K)) = \mathrm{tr}(\tau_* \zeta_*, H_r(K))$$
$$+ \mathrm{tr}(\tau_\# \zeta, B_r(K)) + \mathrm{tr}(\tau_\# \zeta, B_{r-1}(K)).$$

Multiply each term of this equation by $(-1)^r$ and sum from $r = 0$ to $r = n = \dim(K)$ remembering that $B_{-1}(K) = 0 = B_n(K)$. This gives $\sum(-1)^r \mathrm{tr}(\tau_\# \zeta, C_r(K)) = \sum(-1)^r \mathrm{tr}(\tau_* \zeta_*, H_r(K))$. This last equation can be rewritten to give the conclusion of the theorem.

We are now going to use the additive group Q of the rational number field as the coefficient group for homology theory.

DEFINITION 3. The Lefschetz number $L(f, X)$ of a polytope map $f: X \rightarrow X$ is the number

$$\sum (-1)^r \operatorname{tr}(f_*, H_r(X, Q)).$$

By definition, the number is clearly a topological invariant of f and X and Hopf's Theorem shows how to calculate this invariant in terms of a simplicial approximation of f. The proof of the next theorem shows how to take advantage of this situation. By definition the number is a rational number but it may not be at all clear right now that this number is always an integer.

THEOREM 8. The Lefschetz number $L(f, X)$ is an integer.

Proof: Let (K, g) be a triangulation of X, K' a subdivision of K, $\tau: K' \rightarrow K$ a simplicial approximation of $g^{-1}fg$, and $\zeta: C(K) \rightarrow C(K')$ the subdivision chain transformation. In each dimension r, select a basis of $C_r(K)$ consisting of oriented r-simplexes. Then for each basis element s_j^r of $C_r(K)$ we have

$$\zeta_r(s_j^r) = \sum_k b_j^k t_k^r$$

$$\tau_\#(t_k^r) = \sum_i c_k^i s_i^r$$

where each b_j^k and each c_k^i is equal to 0, $+1$, or -1; the first sum is taken over all r-simplexes t_k^r of K', and the second sum is over all r-simplexes s_i^r of K. It follows then that

$$\tau_\# \zeta_r(s_j^r) = \sum_i \sum_k c_k^i b_j^k(s_i^r).$$

Consequently, if $A = (a_j^i)$ is the matrix representing the linear transformation

$$\tau_\# \zeta_r: C_r(K) \rightarrow C_r(K)$$

with respect to the chosen basis, we see that $a_j^i = \sum_k c_k^i b_j^k$ so that A is an integral matrix and $\operatorname{tr}(\tau_\# \zeta_r, C_r(K)) = \sum a_i^i$ is an integer. This is true for each dimension r and therefore the Lefschetz number $\sum (-1)^r \operatorname{tr}(\tau_\# \zeta_r, C_r(K))$ is also an integer.

2. THE EULER–POINCARÉ CHARACTERISTIC

An interesting specialization of Hopf's Theorem is obtained by considering the Lefschetz number of the identity map of a polytope X. If (K, g) is a triangulation of X and $f: X \to X$ is the identity, then $g^{-1}fg$ is the identity map of $|K|$ and the identity simplicial map $\tau: K \to K$ is a simplicial approximation of $g^{-1}fg$. The subdivision homomorphism $\zeta: K \to K$ is also the identity so that the mapping $\tau_\# \zeta: C_r(K) \to C_r(K)$ is the identity transformation. Let $\alpha_r(K)$ be the trace of this identity transformation, or equivalently, the dimension of the vector space $C_r(K)$. Since the elementary integral r-chains form a basis for $C_r(K)$ it is seen that $\alpha_r(K)$ is equal to the number of r-simplexes in the complex K. Next let $\rho_r(X)$ be the dimension of the vector space $H_r(X)$. With this notation we may write Hopf's Theorem specialized to the identity map of $|X|$ as

(1) $$\sum (-1)^r \alpha_r(K) = \sum (-1)^r \rho_r(X).$$

DEFINITION 4. The number $\sum (-1)^r \rho_r(X) = \chi(X)$ is called the Euler–Poincaré characteristic of the polytope X.

The Euler–Poincaré characteristic is a function of the polytope X and is topologically invariant. The first statement means that the characteristic is independent of any triangulation of X and the second means that if X and Y are homeomorphic, then their characteristics are equal. Both these statements follow from the definition and the topological invariance of the homology groups. Now the fact that the numbers $\alpha_r(K)$ are not topological invariants can easily be demonstrated by exhibiting two different triangulations of a polytope. However, Equation (1) shows that the alternating sum of these numbers is invariant.

EXAMPLE 1: In order to compute the Euler–Poincaré characteristic of the two sphere, remember that the nonzero homology groups of S^2 are $H_i(S^2) \approx Q$ for $i = 0, 2$. The numbers $\rho_i(S^2)$ are given by

$$\rho_i(S^2) = \begin{cases} 1 & \text{if } i = 0 \text{ or } 2 \\ 0 & \text{if } i \neq 0 \text{ or } 2. \end{cases}$$

From this, $\chi(S^2) = 2$. This tells us that if (K, g) is any triangulation of S^2, and $\alpha_i(K)$ is the number of i-simplexes in K, then

$$\sum (-1)^i \alpha_i(K) = 2.$$

Let us check this by considering the triangulation of S^2 as the boundary of a 3-simplex. We have $\alpha_0(K) = 4, \alpha_1(K) = 6, \alpha_2(K) = 4$ so that $\sum (-1)^i \alpha_i(K) = 2$ as required.

EXAMPLE 2: The torus T^2, the Klein bottle K, and the projective plane P^2 have characteristics 0, 0, and 1. These values may be verified by looking at the triangulations in Examples 5, 6, and 7 of Chapter I.

EXAMPLE 3: Let X be the space consisting of two circles tangent to each other at a common point. By looking at a triangulation of X we see that $\chi(X) = -1$. Since X has a 1-dimensional triangulation, we know that $\rho_i(X) = 0$ for $i > 1$. Therefore Equation (1) becomes $-1 = \rho_0(X) - \rho_1(X)$. Since X is connected, $\rho_0(X) = 1$ and we see that $\rho_1(X) = 2$. This means that $H_1(X)$ is a 2-dimensional vector space and therefore is isomorphic to $Q \oplus Q$.

EXERCISE 1

1. If $f: X \to Y$ is a nullhomotopic polytope map—that is, if f is homotopic to a map which transforms X into a single point of Y—show that for each $r > 0$ the homomorphism $f_*: H_r(X; G) \to H_r(Y; G)$ is the zero homomorphism.

2. Let X be a space consisting of m circles all tangent at a common point. Show that $H_1(X; Q) \approx Q \oplus \cdots \oplus Q$ for m summands.

3. Prove that $H_1(P^2; Q) \approx H_2(P^2; Q)$.

4. In order to compute the 2-dimensional group $H_2(P^2; G)$ of the projective plane, use the triangulation given in Example 7, Chapter I. A cycle z in $Z_2(P^2; G)$ can be written $z = \sum g^i s_i^2$ where the sum is over the seven 2-simplexes in the triangulation. By considering the consequences of $\partial(z) = 0$, conclude that $g^i = g^j$ for all i and j.

Further conclude that for some i and j, $g^i = -g^j$. It is easy to see from this that $H_2(P^2; G) = Z_2(P^2; G)$ is isomorphic to the subgroup of G consisting of all elements of order two; thus $H_2(P^2, Z) = H_2(P^2; Q) = 0$, $H_2(P^2; Z_2) = Z_2$, and so forth.

5. Prove that the Euler–Poincaré characteristic of a contractible polytope is $+1$. Use this to show that the torus T^2, the Klein bottle K, and the n-sphere S^n are all noncontractible.

3. THE BORSUK–ULAM THEOREM

In this section we give a proof of a famous theorem conjectured by S. Ulam and first proved by Karol Borsuk in 1933. For the purpose of the proof, some preliminary results concerning mappings of spheres will be necessary.

Recall that the n-sphere is defined by

$$S^n = \{(x^1, x^2, \ldots, x^{n+1}) \in R^{n+1} : \sum (x^i)^2 = 1\}.$$

We saw earlier that the triangulation of S^n as the boundary of an $(n + 1)$-simplex was most convenient in computing the homology groups of S^n. A different triangulation of S^n will be better suited for the work of the present section.

To begin, let Q^n be the subset of R^{n+1} given by

$$Q^n = \{(x^1, x^2, \ldots, x^{n+1}) \in R^{n+1} : \sum |x^i| = 1\}.$$

We shall exhibit a complex K^n whose space is Q^n and a homeomorphism $f: Q^n \to S^n$. This will establish K^n as a triangulation of S^n. The following notation shall be used. For each integer $i = 1, 2, \ldots, n + 1$, let a_i be the point of R^{n+1} whose ith coordinate is 1 and all others zero. Let J_{n+1} be the set of integers given by $J_{n+1} = \{1, 2, \ldots, n + 1\}$ and we shall consider functions from J_{n+1} to the set $\{1, -1\}$. For each such function $\pi : J_{n+1} \to \{1, -1\}$ define the simplex s_π^n in R^{n+1} by $s_\pi^n = \langle \pi(1)a_1, \pi(2)a_2, \ldots, \pi(n + 1)a_{n+1}\rangle$; therefore, each s_π^n is contained in Q^n. To see that this is so, consider a point $x = (x^1, x^2, \ldots, x^{n+1})$ of s_π^n. We have then that $x^i = \pi(i)\lambda^i$ where $\{\lambda^i\}$ is the set of barycentric coordinates of x with respect to the set $\{\pi(1)a_1, \pi(2)a_2, \ldots, \pi(n + 1)a_{n+1}\}$. Then $\sum |x^i| = \sum |\pi(i)\lambda^i| = \sum \lambda^i = 1$. This implies that s_π^n is contained in Q^n. Also, since Q^n is a closed set in R^{n+1} the closure of s_π^n is contained in Q^n. Conversely, let $x = (x^1, x^2 \ldots, x^{n+1})$ be an element of Q^n. Select a function $\pi : J_{n+1} \to \{1, -1\}$ such that

$\pi(i) = 1$ if $x^i > 0$ and $\pi(i) = -1$ if $x^i < 0$. Then we have that $x = \sum |x^i|\pi(i)a_i$. This, together with $\sum |x^i| = 1$, implies that x is an element of the closure of s^n_π. Thus we have proved that Q^n is the space of the complex consisting of all nonnull faces of the simplexes s^n_π. It is left as an easy exercise to verify that this collection of simplexes actually is a complex—this is the complex denoted by the symbol K^n.

The next step is to exhibit a homeomorphism between Q^n and S^n. The method is to define mappings $f : Q^n \to S^n$ and $g : S^n \to Q^n$ as follows:

$$f(x^1, x^2, \ldots, x^{n+1}) = (y^1, y^2, \ldots, y^{n+1}) \qquad \text{where } y^i = \frac{x^i}{(\sum (x^i)^2)^{1/2}};$$

$$g(y^1, y^2, \ldots, y^{n+1}) = (x^1, x^2, \ldots, x^{n+1}) \qquad \text{where } x^i = \frac{y^i}{\sum |y^i|}.$$

Then g and f are inverse mappings and it follows that each is a homeomorphism.

We have now established that the complex K^n and the map f provide a triangulation (K^n, f) of the n-sphere. This triangulation is related in a special way to the symmetry map of R^{n+1}.

Let $A : R^{n+1} \to R^{n+1}$ denote the symmetry with respect to the origin. In other words, A is the mapping of R^{n+1} which, in vector notation, sends each point into its negative: $A(x) = -x$. Both Q^n and S^n are A-invariant; that is, they are symmetric with respect to the origin. An element of Q^n or S^n and its image $A(x)$ are called *antipodal* points. The complex K^n can also be said to be symmetric with respect to the origin since s^n_π and $s^n_{-\pi}$ are antipodal simplexes. The symbol A will also be used to represent the simplicial map of K^n which sends each vertex into its antipodal point. Then $A_\#$ denotes the induced chain transformation.

The triangulation (K^n, f) of S^n has been described with the proof of the next theorem in mind.

THEOREM 9. Let $h : S^n \to S^n$ be a continuous function that carries antipodal points into antipodal points; that is, for each element x of S^n, $hA(x) = Ah(x)$. Then the Lefschetz number $L(h, S^n)$ is an even integer.

Proof: Use will be made of the triangulation (K^n, f) of S^n and especially of the fact that $L(h, S^n) = L(f^{-1}hf, Q^n)$. (Recall that Q^n is the space of the complex K^n.) Let K' be a barycentric subdivision of K^n star related to K^n with respect to $f^{-1}hf$ and let $\tau : K' \to K$ be a simplicial approximation of $f^{-1}hf$. In choosing the simplicial mapping τ, we wish to arrange that τ commutes with the symmetry map A. This can be done as follows. Since the subdivision K' is symmetric with respect to the origin, we may separate the vertices of K' into two disjoint sets B and $A(B)$. For each vertex x in B, choose a vertex $\tau(x)$ of K^n such that $f^{-1}hf$ maps the star of x into the star of $\tau(x)$. Next, define $\tau(x)$ for elements in $A(B)$ by $\tau A(x) = A\tau(x)$. It is now easy to see, using the fact that $f^{-1}hf$ maps antipodal points of Q^n into antipodal points, that the simplicial mapping so defined is a simplicial approximation of $f^{-1}hf$, and furthermore, that $\tau A = A\tau$.

The next observation has to do with the subdivision homomorphism $\zeta_r : C_r(K^n) \to C_r(K')$ and the orientation of the complex K'. From the definition of ζ, for each r-simplex s_j^r of K^n, $\zeta_r(s_j^r) = \sum \varepsilon_j^i t_i^r$ where the sum is taken over all r-simplexes of K' contained in s_j^r and ε_j^r is $+1$ or -1. We say that a simplex t_i^r of K' contained in s_j^r is oriented like s_j^r if $\varepsilon_j^i = +1$ and that t_i^r is oriented unlike s_j^r if $\varepsilon_j^i = -1$. We may orient K' so that whenever t_i^r is contained in s_r^r, then t_i^r is oriented like s_j^r if and only if $A(t_i^r)$ is oriented like $A(s_j^r)$. The purpose of this particular orientation is to ensure that ζ commutes with $A_\#$. This can be seen since, for each r-simplex s_j^r of K^k, we have $A_\# \zeta_r(s_j^r) = A_\#(\sum \varepsilon_j^i t_i^r) = \sum \varepsilon_j^i A(t_i^r) = \zeta_r A_\#(s_j^r)$.

We now consider the Lefschetz number $L(f^{-1}hf, Q^n) = \sum (-1)^r \operatorname{tr}(\tau_\# \zeta_r, C_r(K^n))$. Let us examine more closely the number $\operatorname{tr}(\tau_\# \zeta_r, C_r(K^n))$ for a single dimension r. Let $M = (m_j^i)$ be the matrix representing the linear transformation $\tau_\# \zeta_r$ with respect to the basis of $C_r(K^n)$ consisting of the elementary integral r-chains. Then the integer m_j^i is the coefficient of s_j^r in the chain $\tau_\# \zeta_r(s_j^r)$ and the sum of these coefficients is the number $\operatorname{tr}(\tau_\# \zeta_r, C_r(K^n))$. Now it will be shown that each coefficient appears twice in this sum. It will be convenient to let the symbol $g(s_j^r)$ represent the coefficient of s_j^r in the chain $\tau_\# \zeta_r(s_j^r)$. In other words, $g(s_j^r) = m_j^j$. To prove that the integer $\operatorname{tr}(\tau_\# \zeta_r, C_r(K^n))$ is even, it will be enough to show that $g(A(s_j^r)) = g(s_j^r)$. Then

$$\tau_\# \zeta_r(s_j^r) = g(s_j^r)s_j^r + \sum_{i \neq j} m_j^i s_i^r$$

so that

$$\tau_\# \zeta_r(A(s_j^r)) = \tau_\# \zeta_r(A_\#(s_j^r)) = A_\# \tau_\# \zeta_r(s_j^r) = A_\# \{g(s_j^r)s_j^r + \sum_{i \neq j} m_j^i s_j^r\}$$

$$= g(s_j^r)(A(s_j^r)) + \sum_{i \neq j} m_j^i(A(s_i^r)).$$

Since the coefficient of $A(s_j^r)$ in the chain $\tau_\# \zeta_r(A(s_j^r))$ is $g(s_j^r)$, we conclude that $g(A(s_j^r)) = g(s_j^r)$ and that the integer $\mathrm{tr}(\tau_\# \zeta_r, C_r(K^n))$ is even for each dimension r. Consequently, $L(h, S^n) = \sum (-1)^r \mathrm{tr}(\tau_\# \zeta_r, C_r(K^n))$ is an even integer.

THEOREM 10. Let $h: S^n \to S^n$ $(n > 0)$ map antipodal points into antipodal points. Then $\mathrm{tr}(h_*, H_n(S^n))$ is an odd integer.

Proof: Since $H_r(S^n) = 0$ except for $r = 0$ and $r = n$,

$$L(h, S^n) = \sum (-1)^r \mathrm{tr}(h_*, H_r(S^n)) =$$
$$\mathrm{tr}(h_*, H_0(S^n)) + (-1)^n \mathrm{tr}(h_*, H_n(S^n)).$$

Since S^n is connected, we know from Theorem 1 that the homomorphism $h_*: H_0(S^n) \to H_0(S^n)$ is the identity transformation on a one-dimensional vector space and consequently $\mathrm{tr}(h_*, H_0(S^n)) = 1$. Finally, since $L(h, S^n)$ is even (by Theorem 9), it follows that $\mathrm{tr}(h_*, H_n(S^n))$ is odd and the proof is complete.

THEOREM 11. There exists no continuous mapping $h: S^n \to S^{n-1}$ $(n > 0)$ which carries antipodal points into antipodal points.

Proof: The symbol S^{n-1} here is understood to represent the $(n-1)$-sphere contained in S^n given by

$$S^{n-1} = \{(x^1, x^2, \ldots, x^{n+1}) \in S^n : x^{n+1} = 0\}.$$

Suppose that $h: S^n \to S^{n-1}$ carries antipodal points into antipodal points. Let $i: S^{n-1} \to S^n$ be the inclusion map. We then have the following diagram:

$$H_n(S^n) \overset{h_*}{\to} H_n(S^{n-1}) \overset{i_*}{\to} H_n(S^n).$$

The composed map $ih: S^n \to S^n$ carries antipodal points into antipodal points and by Theorem 10 $\mathrm{tr}((ih)_*, H_n(S^n))$ is odd. On the other hand, since the homomorphism $(ih)_* = i_* h_*$ can be factored through the group $H_n(S^{n-1}) = 0$, $(ih)_*$ must be zero homomorphism and $\mathrm{tr}((ih)_*, H_n(S^n))$ must be zero. The contradiction proves that the supposed map cannot exist.

The method of proof employed for Theorem 11 is used frequently in the applications of algebraic topology. A diagram of topological spaces and continuous maps with certain properties is converted by the homology functor H into a diagram of groups and homomorphisms with corresponding properties. If it can be shown that the algebraic diagram is self-contradictory, one infers that the topological situation is impossible. It might seem that such techniques would always lead to negative conclusions (statements that certain things are impossible). Even though this may be true, such statements can frequently be recast to produce significant positive results. For example, Theorem 11 has as an easy corollary the following well known Borsuk–Ulam Theorem.

THEOREM 12. Every continuous mapping of S^n into R^n maps some pair of antipodal points into the same point.

Proof: Vector notation will be used for points in R^n. If $x = (x^1, x^2, \ldots, x^n)$, then $-x = (-x^1, -x^2, \ldots, -x^n)$, and $\|x\|$ denotes the "length" of x: $\|x\| = (\sum (x^i)^2)^{1/2}$. Suppose now that $h : S^n \to R^n$ is a continuous mapping, and for each element x of S^n, $h(x) \neq h(-x)$. A mapping $g : S^n \to S^{n-1}$ may be defined by

$$g(x) = \frac{h(x) - h(-x)}{\|h(x) - h(-x)\|}$$

since $h(x) - h(-x)$ is never zero. It is easily seen that g is continuous and maps antipodal points of S^n into antipodal points of S^{n-1}. This contradicts Theorem 11 and completes the proof.

4. THE LEFSCHETZ FIXED-POINT THEOREM

In its remote beginning algebraic or "combinatorial" topology concerned itself with the study of certain "connectivity" numbers associated with polytopes. The computation of these numbers associated with a particular polytope X was done by means of a triangulating complex K of X. Thus it was realized that the numbers were not, in the strict sense, functions of the polytope X but rather of the triangulating complex K. It was eventually learned that the connectivity numbers could be computed using only the algebraic properties of the homology groups of the complex K. This information, together with the topological invariance of the homology groups, enables one to infer that the connectivity numbers are functions of the polytope and do not depend on the triangulating complex used in the calculation. This result was conjectured around 1900 by the French mathematician Henri Poincaré and it was considered an outstanding honor for the American mathematical community when J. W. Alexander of Princeton University gave the first satisfactory proof.

A little later, another American success story was the proof by Solomon Lefschetz, then at the University of Kansas, of a proposition that has since come to be known as the Lefschetz Fixed-Point Theorem. One version of this theorem will be proved in the present section.

THEOREM 13. Let $f: X \to X$ be a polytope map. If the Lefschetz number $L(f, X)$ is not zero, then the function f has a fixed point, that is, a point x_0 of X such that $f(x_0) = x_0$.

Proof: We make an indirect proof by assuming that there is no fixed point and showing that on the basis of this assumption $L(f, X) = 0$. Since the polytope X is compact, we may assume that (K, g) is a triangulation of X and ε is a positive number such that for each

$$x \in |K|, d(x, g^{-1} fg(x)) > \varepsilon.$$

Let us now arrange that the mesh of K is less than $\varepsilon/3$. This can be done by replacing K with a suitable subdivision if necessary. Furthermore, let K' be a subdivision of K and let $\tau : K' \to K$ be a simplicial approximation of $g^{-1} fg$. We are now going to compute the number $\operatorname{tr}(\tau_\# \zeta, C_r(K))$ for a single dimension r by using as a basis of $C_r(K)$ the set $\{s_i^r\}$ of elementary r-chains.

Let s_k^r be a particular elementary r-chain of K. Then $\zeta(s_k^r) = \sum \varepsilon_k^j t_j^r$ where the summation is over all r-simplexes t_j^r of K' contained in s_k^r. Also,

$$\tau_\# \zeta(s_k^r) = \tau_\# \left(\sum \varepsilon_k^j t_j^r \right) = \sum \varepsilon_k^j \tau_\# (t_j^r) = \sum q_k^i s_i^r.$$

If $q_k^i \neq 0$ for some i, then $s_i^r = \tau_\#(t_j^r)$ for some t_j^r of K' contained in s_k^r. Let v be a vertex of this t_j^r. Then since $g^{-1} fg(v)$ is an element of the star set of $\tau(v)$, we have $d(g^{-1} fg(v), \tau(v)) < \varepsilon/3$ which implies that $d(v, \tau(v)) > 2\varepsilon/3$. Since $\tau(v)$ is a vertex of s_i^r, we infer that t_j^r is not contained in s_i^r so that $s_i^r \neq s_k^r$. To sum up, we have shown that if $q_k^i \neq 0$, then $i \neq k$. In other words, for each i, $q_i^i = 0$; therefore $\operatorname{tr}(\tau_\# \zeta, C_r(K)) = \sum q_i^i = 0$. Finally, $L(f, X) = \sum (-1)^r \operatorname{tr}(\tau_\# \zeta, C_r(K)) = 0$ and this completes the proof.

As an application of the Lefschetz Fixed-Point Theorem we have the following proposition.

THEOREM 14. Let X be a polytope for which $\chi(X) \neq 0$. Let $\rho_r(X)$ be the dimension of the vector space $H_r(X; Q)$. Define $M_0 = \sum \rho_{2r}(X)$ and $M_1 = \sum \rho_{2r+1}(X)$ so that $\chi(X) = M_0 - M_1$. Finally, let $M = \max\{M_0, M_1\}$ and let $f : X \to X$ be a homeomorphism. Then for some positive integer s less than or equal to M, the iterated function $f^s : X \to X$ has a fixed point.

Proof: Let A_r be a matrix representing the nonsingular transformation $f_* : H_r(X; Q) \to H_r(X; Q)$. Then each characteristic root $\lambda_{i,r}$ of A_r is nonzero. Also, A_r^s represents $(f^s)_* : H_r(X; Q) \to H_r(X; Q)$ and the characteristic roots of A_r^s are $\{\lambda_{i,r}^s\}$. Now the cardinality of the indexed family $\{\lambda_{i,2r}\}$ is M_0 and that of $\{\lambda_{i,2r+1}\}$ is M_1. Assume that f^s has no fixed point for $s = 1, 2, \ldots, M$. Then

$$0 = L(f^s, X) = \sum_r \sum_i \lambda_{i,2r}^s - \sum_r \sum_j \lambda_{j,2r+1}^s$$

implies that

$$\sum_r \sum_i \lambda_{i,2r}^s = \sum_r \sum_j \lambda_{j,2r+1}^s.$$

Finally, Newton's formulas expressing the elementary symmetric functions in terms of the sums of the powers show that $M_0 = M_1$. From this we conclude that $\chi(X) = 0$ and this contradiction of the hypothesis proves the theorem.

5. THE BROUWER FIXED-POINT THEOREM

The earliest example of a fixed-point theorem was given by the Dutch mathematician L. E. J. Brouwer. It will be shown here that this proposition is a logical consequence of Theorem 13.

DEFINITION 5. A topological space X has *the fixed-point property* provided every continuous function $f : X \to X$ has a fixed point.

THEOREM 15. (Brouwer) Every closed simplex has the fixed-point property.

This theorem is actually a corollary to a stronger result.

THEOREM 16. Every contractible polytope has the fixed-point property.

Proof: Let $f: X \rightarrow X$ be a mapping of a contractible polytope X. Since $H_r(X, Q) = 0$ for $r > 0$ and since $f_* : H_0(X, Q) \rightarrow H_0(X, Q)$ is the identity mapping of a one-dimensional vector space, we see that $L(f, X) = 1$ and consequently, by Theorem 13, f has a fixed point.

6. THE NO-RETRACTION THEOREM

In this section we present a second proof of the Brouwer Fixed-Point Theorem based on the notion of a retract.

DEFINITION 6. A subset A of a space X is said to be a *retract* of X provided there exists a map $r : X \rightarrow A$ such that $r \mid X = I_A$. The map r is called a *retraction*.

THEOREM 17. A subset A of a space X is a retract of X if and only if every map $f: A \rightarrow Y$ can be extended to X.

The proof is left as an exercise.

THEOREM 18. If X has the fixed-point property and A is a retract of X, then A has the fixed-point property.

The proof is left as an exercise.

THEOREM 19. Let $r : X \rightarrow A$ be a retraction of a polytope X onto a subpolytope A. Then the induced homomorphisms $r_* : H_q(X, G) \rightarrow H_q(A, G)$ are surjective for each dimension r.

ELEMENTARY APPLICATIONS 113

Proof: Let $i : A \to X$ be the inclusion map. Then $ri = I_A$. Now consider the following diagram:

$$H_q(A, G) \overset{i_*}{\to} H_q(X, G) \overset{r_*}{\to} H_q(A, G).$$

Thus $r_* i_* = (ri)_* = (I_A)_* =$ identity and this implies that r_* is surjective.

THEOREM 20. S^{n-1} is not a retract of E^n.

Proof: If $r : E^n \to S^{n-1}$ were a retraction, then the induced homomorphism $r_* : H_{n-1}(E^n) \to H_{n-1}(S^{n-1})$ would be surjective. However, this is impossible for a nontrivial coefficient group G since $H_{n-1}(E^n) = 0$ and $H_{n-1}(S^{n-1})$ is isomorphic to the coefficient group.

THEOREM 21. The following statements are equivalent.

   (i) S^{n-1} is not a retract of E^n.

   (ii) E^n has the fixed-point property.

   (iii) A closed n-simplex has the fixed-point property.

Proof: that (ii) and (iii) are equivalent. This is easy since E^n is homeomorphic to a closed n-simplex.

Proof: that (ii) implies (i). Assume that E^n has the fixed-point property and that S^{n-1} is a retract of E^n. Under these circumstances S^{n-1} must also have the fixed-point property by Theorem 18. However, S^{n-1} does not have the fixed-point property as is evidenced by the existence of the function $f : S^{n-1} \to S^{n-1}$ given by $f(x) = -x$. The contradiction completes the proof of this part.

Proof: that (i) implies (ii). Now assume the existence of a function $f : E^n \to E^n$ having no fixed point and exhibit a retraction $r : E^n \to S^{n-1}$. The idea is fairly simple and goes as follows. For each element x of E^n, the line segment $\langle x, f(x) \rangle$ is contained entirely within E^n and the line $\pi(x, f(x))$ intersects the boundary S^{n-1} in just two points. One of these points is to be designated as $r(x)$ but some care must be exercised in making the choice. Actually, any point y of $\pi(x, f(x))$ can be written

$$y = tx + (1 - t)f(x),$$

and $r(x)$ is chosen as that unique $y \in \pi(x, f(x))$ satisfying the conditions $t \geqslant 1$ and $\|y\| = 1$. The following considerations show that there is indeed exactly one such point. The condition $\|y\| = 1$ is

$$(2) \qquad t^2 x \cdot x + 2(t - t^2)x \cdot f(x) + (1 - t)^2 f(x) \cdot f(x) = 1.$$

(Here the scalar product of vectors u and v is represented by $u \cdot v$). Equation (2) is a quadratic equation in t and an elementary investigation shows that there is exactly one root greater than or equal to one; hence $r(x)$ is uniquely determined. Thus we have defined a function $r : E^n \to S^{n-1}$. Also it can be seen that if x is an element of S^{n-1}, then $t = 1$ is a root of Equation (2) since $x \cdot x = 1$. This means that $r(x) = x$ for $x \in S^{n-1}$. Finally, the continuity of r follows from the continuity of the function f and of the various operations used in the construction. This completes the proof of the theorem.

Since (i) of Theorem 21 is Theorem 20, and since (iii) of Theorem 21 is a statement of the Brouwer Fixed-Point Theorem (Theorem 15), we have in the proof of the present proposition a second proof of the Brouwer Theorem.

EXERCISE 2

1. Prove Theorem 17.
2. Prove Theorem 18.
3. Show that no open subset of R^{n+1} is homeomorphic to a subset of R^n.
4. Show that the projective plane P^2 is not contractible.
5. Show that P^2 has the fixed-point property.
6. Show that every map $f : S^{2n} \to S^{2n}$ of an even dimensional sphere either has a fixed point or interchanges two points.

7. MAPPINGS OF SPHERES

Many applications of homology theory involve maps $f : X \to Y$ where either X or Y or both are spheres in Euclidean spaces. The first two theorems of this section provide simple but extraordinarily useful results concerning mappings of spheres.

THEOREM 22. Two maps f and g of a space X into S^n are homotopic if for each element x of X, $f(x) \neq -g(x)$.

Proof: Under the hypothesis of the theorem, a homotopy from f to g can be given by

$$H(x, t) = \frac{tg(x) + (1 - t)f(x)}{\|tg(x) + (1 - t)f(x)\|}$$

since $\|tg(x) + (1 - t)f(x)\|$ is never zero.

DEFINITION 7. A map $f: X \to Y$ is said to be nullhomotopic or inessential if it is homotopic to a constant map from X to Y.

THEOREM 23. A map $f: S^n \to Y$ is nullhomotopic if and only if f has a continuous extension $F: E^{n+1} \to Y$.

Proof: Consider the equation $H(x, t) = F((1 - t)x)$. On one hand, if H is a homotopy from f to a constant map, then this equation defines the extension F. On the other hand, if the extension F exists, then the equation defines the homotopy H.

THEOREM 24. If a mapping $f: X \to S^n$ is not surjective, then f is nullhomotopic.

Proof: Select a point $a \in S^n - f(X)$. Then by Theorem 22 f is homotopic to the constant map $g: X \to S^n$ given by $g(X) = -a$.

An outstanding unsolved problem in topology is to enumerate the homotopy classes of maps from S^n to S^m. Our next theorem shows that for the special case when n is less than m there is exactly one such class.

THEOREM 25. Any mapping $f: S^n \to S^m$ where n is less than m is nullhomotopic.

Proof: Let S^n and S^m be triangulated as the boundaries of simplexes s^{n+1} and s^{m+1} and consider a simplicial approximation $\tau: S^n \to S^m$

of f. Now the image $|\tau|(S^n)$ is contained in the union of those simplexes of S^m of dimension less than or equal to n and consequently $|\tau|$ is not surjective, and by Theorem 24 it is nullhomotopic. Finally, f is homotopic to $|\tau|$ and is therefore itself nullhomotopic.

The next question to be considered here is that of the possibility of assigning to each polytope X an integer called its dimension. It seems natural to say that if X is homeomorphic to the space of a complex K then the dimension of X is the integer $\dim(K)$. Before this can be done we need to know that two triangulations of X always have the same dimension. The next lemma is a step in that direction.

> **LEMMA 2.** Let (K, f) be a triangulation of a polytope X and let $g : A \to S^n$ be a mapping from a closed subset A of X to S^n. There then exists a subdivision K' of K and a subcomplex L of K' such that A is contained in $f(|L|)$ and there is an extension $G : f(|L|) \to S^n$ of g.

Proof: The map $g : A \to S^n$ may be considered a map from A into R^{n+1}. By Tietze's extension theorem there is an extension $F : X \to R^{n+1}$ of g. Let $U = F^{-1}(R^{n+1} - \{0\})$. There now exists a barycentric subdivision K' of K of sufficiently high order and a subcomplex L of K' that $A \subset f(|L|) \subset U$. Let $G : f(|L|) \to S^n$ be given by $G(x) = F(x)/\|F(x)\|$. Then G is an extension of g.

> **DEFINITION 8.** The q-dimensional *skeleton* K^q of a complex K is the subcomplex consisting of all simplexes of K of dimension less than or equal to q. If (K, f) is a triangulation of a polytope X, then the q-dimensional skeleton of X relative to f is the set $f(|K^q|)$.

> **THEOREM 26.** Let (K, f) be a triangulation of a polytope X and let n be a positive integer. A necessary and sufficient condition for $\dim(K)$ to be less than or equal to n is that every mapping $g : A \to S^n$ from a closed subset A of X has an extension $G : X \to S^n$.

Proof: First assume that $\dim(K) \leqslant n$ and $g : A \to S^n$ is a map from a closed subset of X. Since the dimension of a complex is invariant under barycentric subdivision, we may assume by Lemma 2 that $A = f(|L|)$ where L is a subcomplex of K.

Now for each nonnegative integer q, let $A^q = A \cup X^q$ where X^q is the q-dimensional skeleton of X with respect to f. The idea is to prove that for each q there is an extension of g to A^q—the proof is by induction on q. It is clear that the extension to A^0 exists since $A^0 - A$ is a set consisting of a finite number of isolated points. Assume then that an extension G^q exists to A^q for some q less than $\dim(K)$. Let $\{s_1^{q+1}, \ldots, s_r^{q+1}\}$ be the $(q + 1)$-dimensional simplexes of K. Then G^q is defined on the boundary of each s_i^{q+1} and by Theorem 25 can be extended in turn over each s_i^{q+1}. This gives an extension G^{q+1} to A^{q+1}. By induction there exists an extension to A^m where $m = \dim(K)$ and thus $A^m = X$. This completes the proof of necessity.

To start the sufficiency proof, assume that $\dim(K) > n$ and let $A = f(B)$ where B is the boundary of an $(n + 1)$-dimensional simplex s^{n+1} of K. Also let E be the image under f of the closure of s^{n+1}. Then E is an $(n + 1)$-cell with boundary A. There exists a homeomorphism $g : A \to S^n$. If there were an extension $G : E \to S^n$ of g, then the composite $g^{-1}G : E \to A$ would be a retraction of E onto A which would contradict Theorem 20. This completes the proof of the theorem.

The next theorem is an immediate corollary of Theorem 26.

THEOREM 27. If (K_1, f_1) and (K_2, f_2) are triangulations of a polytope X, then $\dim(K_1) = \dim(K_2)$.

DEFINITION 9. The dimension of a polytope X is $\dim(K)$ where (K, f) is any triangulation of X.

The final application of homology theory in this section will be the result that open subsets U and V of R^m and R^n are not homeomorphic for m and n unequal. The proof will be preceded by several theorems each having considerable interest in its own right.

THEOREM 28. Let (X, A) be a compact pair (that is, X is a compact topological space and A is closed in X). Then every nullhomotopic map $f : A \to S^n$ has an extension to X.

Proof: Let $H : A \times I \to S^n$ be a homotopy from f to a constant map $g : A \to S^n$ given by $g(A) = y_0$. Consider the map $F : A \times I \cup X \times 1 \to S^n$ given by $F(a, t) = H(a, t)$, $F(x, 1) = y_0$. This map has an extension $F' : P \to S^n$ where P is an open set in $X \times I$ containing $A \times I \cup X \times 1$. To see that this is so, first observe that F has an extension $G : X \times I \to R^{n+1}$. Next, let $P = G^{-1}(R^{n+1} - \{0\})$ and let $r : (R^{n+1} - \{0\}) \to S^n$ be the retraction given by $r(x) = x/\|x\|$. Then F' is defined as the composition rG. Now there exists a set Q open in X containing A and such that $Q \times I$ is contained in P. Since X is normal, there exists a map $\theta : X \to I$ such that $\theta | A = 1$ and $\theta | (X - Q) = 0$. Finally, the map $\bar{f} : X \to S^n$ given by $\bar{f}(x) = F'(x, 1 - \theta(x))$ is an extension of f to X.

THEOREM 29. (Borsuk's Separation Theorem) Let X be a compact subset of R^n and let x_0 be an element of $R^n - X$. In order that x_0 be in the unbounded component of $R^n - X$, it is necessary and sufficient that the mapping $p : X \to S^{n-1}$ given by

$$p(x) = \frac{x - x_0}{\|x - x_0\|}$$

be nullhomotopic.

Proof: We may assume that the point x_0 is the origin in R^n and that X lies in the interior of E^n. Then the map p is given by $p(x) = x/\|x\|$.

First suppose that x_0 is in the unbounded component C of $R^n - X$. Since the open connected set C is arcwise connected, there exists a mapping $f : I \to C$ such that $f(0) = x_0$, $f(1) = x_1$ where x_1 is an element of $R^n - E^n$. Now the mapping $H : X \times I \to S^{n-1}$ given by $H(x, t) = (x - f(t))/\|x - f(t)\|$ is a homotopy from $p(x)$ to a mapping $g : X \to S^{n-1}$ given by $g(x) = (x - x_1)/\|x - x_1\|$. Also $x_1/\|x_1\|$ is an element of S^{n-1}, and if it were true for some $x \in X$ that $g(x) = x_1/\|x_1\|$, then it would follow that

$$x = \left(\frac{\|x - x_1\|}{x_1} + 1\right)x_1.$$

This, however, is impossible since $x \in E^n$ and $x_1 \notin E^n$. This means that $g(x)$ is not surjective and is therefore nullhomotopic. Consequently, the map p is also nullhomotopic.

Next assume that p is nullhomotopic and that the component C of $R^n - X$ containing x_0 is bounded. Since $(C \cup X, X)$ is a compact pair, by Theorem 28 p has an extension $p' : C \cup X \to S^{n-1}$. This map p' has a further extension $p'' : E^n \to S^{n-1}$ given by

$$p''(x) = x/\|x\| \qquad \text{for } x \in E^n - C.$$

We now observe that p'' is a retraction of E^n onto S^{n-1} which is impossible by Theorem 20. This contradiction completes the proof of the theorem.

THEOREM 30. (Borsuk) Let X be a closed proper subset of S^n. The set $S^n - X$ is connected if and only if every map $f : X \to S^{n-1}$ is nullhomotopic.

Proof: First suppose that $S^n - X$ is not connected and that x_0, x_1 are points in distinct components of $S^n - X$. If we identify $S^n - x_1$ with R^n, then x_0 lies in a bounded component of $R^n - X$. Consequently, by Theorem 29 there exists an essential (not nullhomotopic) map $p : X \to S^{n-1}$.

Next suppose that $S^n - X$ is connected and consider a mapping $f : X \to S^{n-1}$. By Theorem 27 we may suppose that S^n is the space of an n-complex K and that $X = |L|$ where L is a proper subcomplex of K. Furthermore, by Theorem 26 we may assume that f is defined on $X \cup |K^{n-1}|$ (K^{n-1} is the $(n-1)$-skeleton of K). Let $\{s_1^n, s_2^n, \ldots, s_q^n\}$ be the open n-simplexes of K and let p_i be the centroid of s_i^n. For each s_i^n there is a retraction $r_i : |K| - p_i \to |K| - s_i^n$ and an extension f_i of f to $X \cup |K^{n-1}| \cup (s_i^n - p_i)$ can be given by $f_i(x) = fr_i(x)$. Thus f can be extended to $S^n - \{x_0, x_1, \ldots, x_t\}$ where the x_i are those p_i contained in $S^n - X$. The next step is to show that f can be extended to $S^n - \{x_1, \ldots, x_t\}$. To see that this is so, we observe that there exists a finite sequence of points

$$x_0 = y_0, y_1, y_2, \ldots, y_k = x_1$$

and a sequence of n-cells $E_1, E_2, \ldots, E_k$ in $S^n - X$ such that $y_{j-1}, y_j \in E_j$ for $j = 1, 2, \ldots, k$, and the boundary of E_j contains none of the x's or y's. Suppose now that f has been extended to $S^n - \{y_j, x_1, x_2, \ldots, x_t\}$. There is a retraction $r : S^n - y_{j+1} \to S^n - E_{j+1}^n$ and an extension $\bar{f}$ of f to $S^n - \{y_{j+1}, x_1, x_2, \ldots, x_t\}$ can be given by $\bar{f}(x) = fr(x)$. By induction, then, f

can be extended to $S^n - \{x_1, \ldots, x_t\}$. A repetition of this process leads to an extension of f to the set $S^n - x_t$.

Finally, $S^n - x_t$, being homeomorphic to R^n, is contractible and the existence of an extension of f to such a set implies that f is nullhomotopic.

THEOREM 31. (The Invariance of Domain Theorem) Let U and V be homeomorphic subsets of S^n. If U is open in S^n, then V is also open in S^n.

Proof: Let $h : U \to V$ be a homeomorphism. Choose an element y of V. Then $y = h(x)$ for some $x \in U$ and since U is open there exists a closed neighborhood N of x with boundary B such that (N, B) is homeomorphic to (E^n, S^{n-1}) and N is contained in U. Let $X = h(N)$, $A = h(B)$. Then (X, A) is homeomorphic to (E^n, S^{n-1}). Since every map of E^n into S^{n-1} is nullhomotopic, by Theorem 30, $S^n - X$ is connected. On the other hand, the identity map $S^{n-1} \to S^{n-1}$ is essential and again by Theorem 30 $S^n - A$ is not connected. The set $X - A$, being homeomorphic to $E^n - S^{n-1}$, is connected. Also, $S^n - A = (S^n - X) \cup (X - A)$ and this, together with the connectedness of $S^n - X$ and $X - A$, implies that these two sets are components of $S^n - A$. In particular, $X - A$ is a neighborhood of the point y contained in V and this provides that V is open.

THEOREM 32. Open sets U and V of R^n and R^m are not homeomorphic if m and n are distinct.

Proof: If n is less than m, then R^n can be embedded in R^m as a nowhere dense subset. Consequently, no open set in R^m can be homeomorphic to a subset of R^n.

8. THE DEGREE OF A MAP

We have seen in Theorem 25 that each map $f : S^n \to S^m$ is nullhomotopic provided n is less than m and it follows that there is just one homotopy class of such maps. The enumeration of the homotopy classes for the case $n = m$ depends on the notion of the degree of a map. The first step in the development here will be the proof of the proposition that if

(K, h) is a triangulation of S^n, then K is an orientable n-dimensional pseudomanifold. The three parts of the next theorem correspond to the three items in Definition 18, Chapter I.

THEOREM 33. Let (K, h) be a triangulation of S^n. Then the following hold true.

(a) Each simplex of K is a face of an n-simplex.

(b) Each $(n - 1)$-simplex of K is a face of exactly two n-simplexes.

(c) For each pair t_1^n, t_2^n of n-simplexes in K there exists a finite sequence $s_1^n, s_1^{n-1}, \ldots, s_{k-1}^{n-1}, s_k^n$ of simplexes in K such that $s_1^n = t_1^n, s_k^n = t_2^n$, and each s_i^{n-1} is a face of s_i^n and s_{i+1}^n.

Proof of (a): Let t^r be a simplex of K, and among those simplexes having t^r as a face let t^q be a simplex of maximum dimension q. Let x be an element of t^q. Then, on the one hand, x has a neighborhood homeomorphic to an open set in R^q. On the other hand, since (K, h) is a triangulation of S^n, it follows that x has a neighborhood homeomorphic to an open set in R^n. Then by Theorem 32 $q = n$ and this completes the proof of (a).

Proof of (b): Let t^{n-1} be an $(n - 1)$-simplex of K. By part (a), t^{n-1} is a face of at least one n-simplex. Let us show that t^{n-1} cannot be a face of more than two n-simplexes. For this purpose, assume that t^{n-1} is a face of distinct n-simplexes t_1^n and t_2^n. The set $t_1^n \cup t^{n-1} \cup t_2^n$ can be embedded as an open set in R^n, and by invariance of domain this implies that $t_1^n \cup t^{n-1} \cup t_2^n$ is open in $|K|$. If t^{n-1} were a face of an n-simplex t_3^n distinct from t_1^n and t_2^n, then each open set intersecting t^{n-1} (in particular the set $t_1^n \cup t^{n-1} \cup t_2^n$) would intersect t_3^n. This however is impossible and shows that t^{n-1} is a face of not more than two n-simplexes. To complete the proof of part (b) it must be shown that t^{n-1} cannot be a face of exactly one n-simplex. This is left as an exercise.

Proof of (c): First choose a nonzero integral cycle c of $Z_n(K; Z)$ given by $c = \sum g^i s_i^n$ where the sum is over all oriented n-simplexes of K. Furthermore, we may assume that K is oriented in such a way that each g^i is nonnegative. Now let t^{n-1} be an $(n - 1)$-dimensional face of distinct simplexes t_1^n and t_2^n. We have

$$0 = \partial c(t^{n-1}) = [t_1^n, t^{n-1}]g^1 + [t_2^n, t^{n-1}]g^2.$$

Since the absolute value of each incidence number is one, it follows that $g^1 = g^2$ and consequently, $[t_1^n, t^{n-1}] = -[t_2^n, t^{n-1}]$. Since t^{n-1} is an arbitrary $(n-1)$-simplex, this implies that the sum of all n-simplexes $\sum s_i^n$ is an integral n-cycle.

Now let s_0^n be a fixed n-simplex of K and denote by $N = \{s_0^n, \ldots, s_k^n\}$ the collection of all n-simplexes that can be joined to s_0^n by a chain as in the statement of part (c). Let $M = \{s_{k+1}^n, \ldots, s_r^n\}$ represent the remaining n-simplexes. We need to show that the set M is empty. If this were not so we would have linearly independent cycles

$$c_1 = \sum_{i=0}^{k} s_i^n \quad \text{and} \quad c_2 = \sum_{i=k+1}^{r} s_i^n.$$

That is, if g^1, g^2 are integers such that $g^1 c_1 + g^2 c_2 = 0$, then $g^1 = g^2 = 0$. In this case the group $Z_n(K; Z) = H_n(K; Z)$ would contain a free abelian subgroup on two generators c_1 and c_2. This however is impossible since $Z_n(K; Z)$ is infinite cyclic. This completes the proof.

In the course of the proof of Theorem 33 it was seen that if (K, h) is a triangulation of S^n, then K can be oriented in such a way that the sum of all n-simplexes $\sum s_i^n$ is an integral cycle. This property of S^n is used in the definition of the degree of a map. The cycle $c^n = \sum s_i^n$ is called a fundamental n-cycle of K and if $\eta : Z_n(K; Z) \to Z_n(K; Z)$ is any homomorphism, then $\eta(c^n) = m \cdot c^n$ for some integer m.

DEFINITION 10. Let $f : S^n \to S^n$ be a map. There exists an integer m such that the induced homomorphism $f_* : H_n(S^n; Z) \to H_n(S^n; Z)$ is given by $f_*(z) = m \cdot z$ for each $z \in H_n(S^n; Z)$. This integer m is called the degree of the map f (written $\deg(f)$).

The next proposition gives an alternative geometric characterization of the degree of a map which is useful in many applications. Actually, the alternative description was the definition of degree as originally given by L. E. J. Brouwer.

THEOREM 34. Let $f : S^n \to S^n$ $(n > 0)$ be a map with degree m. Let (K, h) be a triangulation of S^n, let K' be a subdivision of K star related to K with respect to the map $h^{-1}fh$, and let $\tau : K' \to K$ be a simplicial approximation of $h^{-1}fh$. Let $\{s_i^n\}$ be the n-simplexes of K oriented so that $\sum s_i^n$ is a cycle. Let each n-simplex of K' be oriented like the n-simplex of K containing it. Finally, for each n-simplex s_i^n of K let a_i be the number of n-simplexes of K' mapped by τ onto s_i^n with orientation preserved, and let b_i be the number of n-simplexes of K' mapped onto s_i^n with orientation reversed. Then for each i, $a_i - b_i = m = \deg(f)$.

Before the proof of Theorem 34 is begun, the comment will be made that this theorem was essentially the justification of the original definition of degree. Brouwer actually defined the degree to be $a_i - b_i$ for some s_i^n and then it had to be shown that this number does not depend on any of the various choices made in its calculation. These choices are the triangulation (K, h), the subdivision K', the simplicial approximation τ, and the particular simplex s_i^n. The statement that the final result is independent of these choices is sometimes called Brouwer's fundamental theorem on the degree of a map. In the present treatment, the degree is defined in a way that obviously depends only on the map f and Theorem 34 states the equivalence with the original definition. Actually, in view of our previous results, the degree of f depends only on the homotopy class of f.

Proof of Theorem 34: Let (K, h) be a triangulation of S^n and K' a subdivision of K star related to K with respect to the map $h^{-1}fh$ and let $\tau : K' \to K$ be a simplicial approximation of $h^{-1}fh$. We now have by Theorem 27 that $B_n(K; Z)$ is the zero group. It follows that $Z_n(K; Z)$ equals $H_n(K; Z)$ and that the homomorphisms $\tau_\# \zeta : Z_n(K; Z) \to Z_n(K; Z)$ and $\tau_* \zeta_* : H_n(K; Z) \to H_n(K; Z)$ are the same. The cycle $c^n = \sum s_i^n$ is an element of the group $Z_n(K; Z) = H_n(K; Z)$ and we shall compute the image of this element under the homomorphism above in two different ways.

In the first place, from the definitions of τ_* and ζ, for each n-simplex s_j^n of K, $\tau_\# \zeta(s_j) = \sum g_j^i s_i^n$ where g_j^i equals the number of n-simplexes of K' contained in s_j^n and mapped by τ onto s_i^n with orientation preserved minus the number of n-simplexes of K' contained in s_j^n and mapped onto s_i^n with orientation reversed. Therefore we have

$$\tau_\# \zeta(c^n) = \tau_\# \zeta(\sum s_i^n) = \sum (a_i - b_i)s_i^n$$

where a_i and b_i are as in the statement of the theorem.

On the other hand, we have

$$\tau_\# \zeta(c^n) = \tau_* \zeta_*(c^n) = mc^n = \sum ms_i^n.$$

A comparison of these formulas shows that $a_i - b_i = m$ for each $s_i^n \in K$, and the proof is complete.

An immediate application of the geometric characterization of degree is the following proposition.

THEOREM 35. Let $f: S^n \to S^n$ $(n > 0)$ be a map of degree m. Then for each coefficient group G, the homomorphism

$$f_* : H_n(S^n; G) \to H_n(S^n; G)$$

is given by $f_*(z) = mz$.

COROLLARY. $\deg(f) = tr(f_*, H_n(S^n; Q))$

$$L(f, S^n) = 1 + (-1)^n \deg(f).$$

EXERCISE 3

1. Show that the symmetry map $A : S^n \to S^n$ has degree $(-1)^{n+1}$.

2. Show that every map $f: S^n \to S^n$ of even degree has a fixed point.

3. Show that every map $f: S^n \to S^n$ of degree not equal to $(-1)^{n+1}$ has a fixed point.

4. Show that, for every pair of maps $f, g : S^n \to S^n$, $\deg(fg) = \deg(f)$ $\deg(g)$.

5. Show that homotopic maps $f, g : S^n \to S^n$ have the same degree.

6. Show that, if $f: S^n \to S^n$ maps no pair of antipodal points into the same point, then the map $h : S^n \to S^n$ given by

$$h(x) = \frac{(f(x) - f(-x))}{\|f(x) - f(-x)\|}$$

is homotopic to f. Use Theorem 22.

7. Show that every map $f: S^n \to S^n$ of even degree maps some pair of antipodal points into the same point. Hint: Consider the function h of Problem 6.

8. Show that every map $f: S^n \to S^n$ of odd degree maps some pair of antipodal points into antipodal points.

9. Show that for every pair of maps $f, g : S^{2n} \to S^{2n}$ of an even dimensional sphere, at least one of f, g, fg has a fixed point.

9. SUSPENSION

Further progress in the investigation of mappings of spheres depends on the concept of the suspension of a complex. This is a construction which enlarges a given complex K by adding to it two new vertices in a prescribed manner. Then K becomes a subcomplex of the new complex $S(K)$ called the suspension of K.

To start the description of the process, let us first assume that the polytope $|K|$ is contained in Euclidean space R^n and that R^n is in turn the subset of R^{n+1} given by the equation $x^{n+1} = 0$. Let R_+^{n+1} and R_-^{n+1} be the open half spaces of R^{n+1} given by the inequalities $x^{n+1} > 0$ and $x^{n+1} < 0$. Next select points a and b in R_+^{n+1} and R_-^{n+1} respectively. The complex $S(K)$ is now described as follows. First, $S(K)$ contains all simplexes of K. Second, if $\{a_0, a_1, \ldots, a_r\}$ are vertices of a simplex of K, then the sets $\{a, a_0, a_1, \ldots, a_r\}$ and $\{b, a_0, a_1, \ldots, a_r\}$ are geometrically independent and $S(K)$ contains the simplexes spanned by these sets. Finally, $S(K)$ contains the 0-simplexes $\{a\}$ and $\{b\}$.

The polytope $|S(K)|$ is the union of all closed line segments of the forms $\langle a, x \rangle$ and $\langle b, x \rangle$ where x is an element of $|K|$. The union of the segments $\langle a, x \rangle$ is the space of the cone $a * K$ over K with vertex a. Thus $|S(K)|$ is the union of two cones over K with vertices a and b. The points a and b are called the vertices of the suspension $S(K)$. The polytope $|S(K)|$ is called the suspension of the polytope $|K|$.

THEOREM 36. The cone over S^n is E^{n+1} and the suspension of S^n is S^{n+1}.

Proof: A more detailed statement of the theorem is this: If $|K|$ is homeomorphic to S^n, then $|a * K|$ is homeomorphic to E^{n+1} and $|S(K)|$ is homeomorphic to S^{n+1}. To start the proof let $f: |K| \to S^n$ be a homeomorphism. Let S^n be the equator of S^{n+1} and let p and $-p$ be the poles of S^{n+1}. That is, S^n is the subset given by $x^1 = 0$, p and $-p$ are the points $(1, 0, \ldots, 0)$ and $(-1, 0, \ldots, 0)$. A point y of $|S(K)|$ is either of the form $y = ta + (1 - t)x$ or $y = tb + (1 - t)x$ where $0 \leqslant t \leqslant 1$ and $x \in |K|$. Now a function $F: |S(K)| \to S^{n+1}$ is defined by mapping the segment

$\langle a, x \rangle$ onto the minor arc $\langle p, f(x) \rangle$ and the segment $\langle b, x \rangle$ onto the minor arc $\langle -p, f(x) \rangle$. The actual formulas are

$$F(ta + (1 - t)x) = \frac{tp + (1 - t)f(x)}{\|tp + (1 - t)f(x)\|}$$

$$F(tb + (1 - t)x) = \frac{t(-p) + (1 - t)f(x)}{\|t(-p) + (1 - t)f(x)\|}.$$

The mapping so defined is a homeomorphism and maps $|a * K|$ homeomorphically onto the upper hemisphere E_+^{n+1}. That is,

$$E_+^{n+1} = \{(x^1, x^2, \ldots, x^{n+2}) \in S^{n+1} : x^1 \geqslant 0\}.$$

It is easy to see that this set is homeomorphic to the cell E^{n+1}.

DEFINITION 11. Let $f: |K| \to |L|$ be a polytope map. Let a, b be the vertices of $S(K)$, and a', b' the vertices of $S(L)$. The suspension of f is the map

$$S(f) : |S(K)| \to |S(L)|$$

given by

$$S(f)(ta + (1 - t)x) = ta' + (1 - t)f(x)$$
$$S(f)(tb + (1 - t)x) = tb' + (1 - t)f(x).$$

Many applications of the notion of the suspension of a map to homotopy theory derive from the next theorem.

THEOREM 37. If f and g are homotopic polytope maps, then $S(f)$ is homotopic to $S(g)$.

Proof: Let f and g be maps from $|K|$ to $|L|$ and let $H : |K| \times I \to |L|$ be a homotopy from f to g. A map

$$S(H) : |S(K)| \times I \to |S(L)|$$

is defined by

$$S(H)(x, t) = S(H^t(x)).$$

We see that $S(H)(x, 0) = S(H^0)(x) = S(f)(x)$ and that $S(H)(x, 1) = S(H^1)(x) = S(g)(x)$. Thus $S(H)$ is a homotopy from $S(f)$ to $S(g)$.

The plan for the remainder of the present section is to use the geometric characterization of the degree of a map to prove that for each map $f: S^n \to S^n$, the degree of f is equal to the degree of the suspended map $S(f): S^{n+1} \to S^{n+1}$.

Certain preliminary work will be necessary. Recall that if (K, g) is a triangulation of S^n, then the n-simplexes of K may be oriented in such a way that $c^n = \sum s_i^n$ is an integral cycle called a fundamental cycle of K to express the fact that every cycle in $C_n(K; G)$ is of the form gc^n.

We now wish to consider a triangulation (K, g) of S^n and the suspension complex $S(K)$. The complex K will always be oriented so that $\sum s_i^n = c^n$ is a cycle. The vertices of the suspension $S(K)$ will be indicated by a and b. For each r-simplex $\Delta(a_0, a_1, \ldots, a_r)$ of K, the $(r+1)$-simplexes $\Delta(a, a_0, a_1, \ldots, a_r)$ and $\Delta(b, a_0, a_1, \ldots, a_r)$ of $S(K)$ are denoted by as^r and bs^r respectively. An orientation of $S(K)$ is determined by the following rules. First let each simplex of K be oriented in $S(K)$ as it is in K. The description of the orientation of $S(K)$ is completed by assigning incidence numbers

$$[as^r : s^r] = +1$$
$$[bs^r : s^r] = -1.$$

An $(n+1)$-simplex of $S(K)$ can be written as_i^n or bs_i^n and we wish to show that $\sum as_i^n + \sum bs_i^n$ is a fundamental $(n+1)$-cycle of $S(K)$ when the orientation is that described above. To do this it will be sufficient to show that $\sum as_i^n + \sum bs_i^n$ is a cycle. The plan is to define for each $r = 0, 1, \ldots, n$ a homomorphism

$$D: C_r(K; Z) \to C_{r+1}(S(K); Z)$$

by $D(s^r) = as^r + bs^r$. The definition is extended to all of $C_r(K; Z)$ by additivity.

An easy calculation shows that for each r-simplex of K, $\partial D(s^r) = -D \partial(s^r)$, and this relation extends by additivity to all of $C_r(K; Z)$; that is,

$$\partial D(c^r) = -D \partial(c^r).$$

We now have by definition that $D(c^n) = \sum as_i^n + \sum bs_i^n$ and by the equation above that D maps cycles into cycles. Therefore $\sum as_i^n + \sum bs_i^n$ is indeed a cycle of $S(K)$.

In the statement of the next theorem, K' will be a subdivision of a complex K whose space $|K|$ is an n-sphere. The complexes $S(K')$ and $S(K)$ will be oriented in the manner just described.

THEOREM 38. Let $\tau : K' \to K$ be a simplicial map. Then $S(|\tau|) : |S(K')| \to |S(K)|$ is a simplicial map and the degree of $S(|\tau|)$ is equal to the degree of $|\tau|$.

Proof: Let a', b' be the vertices of $S(K')$ and a, b the vertices of $S(K)$. It is clear that $S(|\tau|)$ is simplicial since $S(|\tau|)$ maps a' onto a, b' onto b, and agrees with $|\tau|$ on $|K'|$. To compute the degree of $S(|\tau|)$, select an $(n + 1)$-simplex as^n of $S(K)$ where $s^n = \langle a_0, a_1, \ldots, a_n \rangle$ is an oriented n-simplex of K. Now an $(n + 1)$-simplex $a't^n = \langle a', b_0, b_1, \ldots, b_n \rangle$ of $S(K')$ is mapped by $S(|\tau|)$ onto as^n with orientation preserved if and only if $\{\tau(b_0), \tau(b_1), \ldots, \tau(b_n)\}$ is an even permutation of the set $\{a_0, a_1, \ldots, a_n\}$. This in turn is true if and only if t^n is mapped by τ onto s^n with orientation preserved. Likewise, $a't^n$ is mapped onto as^n with orientation reversed if and only if t^n is mapped onto s^n with orientation reversed. From this it follows easily that the degree of $S(|\tau|)$ is equal to the degree of $|\tau|$.

THEOREM 39. Let $f : S^n \to S^n$ be a map. Then the degree of f is equal to the degree of $S(f)$.

Proof: Let S^n be represented as the space of a complex K so that $f : |K| \to |K|$. Let $\tau : K' \to K$ be a simplicial approximation of f. Then $|\tau|$ and $S(|\tau|)$ are homotopic respectively to f and $S(f)$. Consequently, the degree of $|\tau|$ equals the degree of f and the degree of $S(|\tau|)$ equals the degree of $S(f)$. Finally, we have by Theorem 38 that the degree of $|\tau|$ equals the degree of $S(|\tau|)$. This completes the proof.

10. DEGREE AND HOMOTOPY

In this section a proof will be given of the result, due to H. Hopf, that two maps f, $g : S^n \to S^n$ are homotopic if and only if they have the same degree. This will lead quickly to an enumeration of the homotopy classes of maps from S^n to S^n. The methods used will be "geometric" in that some appeal will be made to visualization. In this connection the language and terminology of geography are very useful in that they enable one to follow rather easily complicated arguments involving spheres. For example, the point p of S^n whose $(n + 1)$th coordinate is $+1$ and the rest zero is called the north pole of S^n and the negative $-p$ of this point is called the south pole. The subsets

$$E_+^n = \{(x^1, x^2, \ldots, x^{n+1}) \in S^n : x^{n+1} \geqslant 0\}$$

$$E_-^n = \{(x^1, x^2, \ldots, x^{n+1}) \in S^n : x^{n+1} \leqslant 0\}$$

are called the northern and southern hemispheres of S^n. It is clear that E_+^n and E_-^n are both homeomorphic to the n-cell E^n. The set $S^{n-1} = E_+^n \cap E_-^n$ is called the equator of S^n.

If x and y are nonantipodal points of S^n, the vector space $V(x, y)$ is a two-dimensional subspace of R^{n+1} and the set $V(x, y) \cap S^n$ is a circle called a great circle of S^n. In defining a homotopy one might speak of pushing the point x along the minor arc of this great circle until it reaches the point y. Ideas such as this can be written out explicitly by taking a little trouble but the more descriptive language is an immense help. As a matter of fact, during the presentation of an involved proof it becomes impracticable to write out all the details. However, an expositor who avails himself of the more descriptive style and decides not to write out the details should provide sufficient information to enable the interested reader to do so for himself.

In the proof of the next theorem, a middle-of-the-road approach will be used. That is, more details will be given than is the usual custom, yet some use will be made of the descriptive terminology. In particular, the following obvious proposition will be used.

LEMMA 3. If a and b are distinct nonantipodal points of S^n and x is a point on the minor arc of the great circle determined by a and b, then the line segment from the center of S^n to the point x intersects the chord $\langle a, b \rangle$ in a point $ta + (1 - t)b$ where $0 \leqslant t \leqslant 1$, and then $x = (ta + (1 - t)b)/\|ta + (1 - t)b\|$.

THEOREM 40. Let A be a closed proper subset of S^n. There exists a homeomorphism $f: S^n \to S^n$ such that f and f^{-1} are both homotopic to the identity map of S^n and $f(A)$ is contained in the interior of E_+^n.

Proof: We may assume that the south pole $-p$ is not an element of A. (This means that we can select a point a not in A and then choose a coordinate system in R^{n+1} so that the $(n + 1)$th coordinate of a is -1.)

There exists a positive number δ such that the closure of the δ-neighborhood of $-p$ does not intersect A. Let N represent this neighborhood and B its boundary in S^n. That is, $B = \{x \in S^n : d(x, -p) = \delta\}$. Now let x represent any point of S^n other than p or $-p$. Let $(p, x, -p)$ represent the semicircular arc of the great circle containing $p, x, -p$. This arc intersects B and S^{n-1} each in a single point denoted by $u(x)$ and $v(x)$ respectively. Now if x is an element of $\bar{N}$, then for some t $(0 \leqslant t \leqslant 1)$

$$x = \frac{t(-p) + (1 - t)u(x)}{\|t(-p) + (1 - t)u(x)\|}$$

and if x is not an element of N, then for some t,

$$x = \frac{tu(x) + (1 - t)p}{\|tu(x) + (1 - t)p\|}.$$

A function $f: S^n \to S^n$ is defined by

$$f(x) = \begin{cases} \dfrac{t(-p) + (1 - t)v(x)}{\|t(-p) + (1 - t)v(x)\|} & \text{if } x \in \bar{N} \\[2ex] \dfrac{tv(x) + (1 - t)p}{\|tv(x) + (1 - t)p\|} & \text{if } x \notin N. \end{cases}$$

The definition of the function f is completed by setting $f(p) = p$ and $f(-p) = -p$. It is routine to verify that the function f is continuous, bijective, and $f(A) \subset E_+^n$. Finally, since neither f nor f^{-1} maps any point into its antipode, then both are homotopic to the identity map of S^n.

A verbal description of the function f may be given by saying that it maps each minor arc $(-p, u(x))$ linearly onto the arc $(-p, v(x))$ and each minor arc $(u(x), p)$ linearly onto the arc $(v(x), p)$.

THEOREM 41. Let $f: S^n \to S^n$ be a map where $n \geqslant 2$. There exists a map $g: S^n \to S^n$ such that f is homotopic to g, and for some $q \in S^n$, $g^{-1}(q)$ is either empty or consists of a single point.

Proof: Let us assume that S^n is the space of a complex K and $f = |\tau|$ for some simplicial map $\tau: K' \to K$. Choose q to be in some open n-simplex of K and then $f^{-1}(q)$ has at most one point in each closed n-simplex of K'. Therefore $f^{-1}(q)$ is a finite set $\{p_1, p_2, \ldots, p_k\}$ and by Theorem 40 we may assume that this set is contained in E_+^n. We now identify E^n_+ with the n-cell E^n so that we may speak of the straight line segment from p_1 to p_i for $i = 2, \ldots, k$. Let L be the union of these segments. That is, $L = \cup_{i=2}^{k} \langle p_1, p_i \rangle$ where $\langle p_1, p_i \rangle$ represents the closed segment from p_1 to p_i. Since f is simplicial we see that $f(L)$ is a 1-dimensional polytope and therefore $f(L) \neq S^n$. It follows that there is an ε-neighborhood U of L in S^n such that $f(\overline{U}) \neq S^n$ and again by Theorem 40 we may assume that $f(\overline{U}) \subset E^n_+$.

The next step is to show that there is a map $\Phi : S^n \to S^n$ homotopic to f and such that $\Phi^{-1}(q) = L$. To this end let $\mu : S^n \to I$ be the map $\mu(x) = (\min(d(x, L), \varepsilon))/\varepsilon$. Now the map Φ is defined by

$$\Phi(x) = \frac{\mu(x)f(x) + (1 - \mu(x))p_1}{\|\mu(x)f(x) + (1 - \mu(x))p_1\|}.$$

It is easy to see that $\Phi^{-1}(q) = L$. Also Φ is homotopic to f since Φ and f are never antipodal.

Now a continuous function $h : (S^n, L) \to (S^n, p_1)$ which maps $S^n - L$ homeomorphically onto $S^n - p_1$ is given by

$$h(x) = \frac{\mu(x) \cdot x + (1 - \mu(x))p_1}{\|\mu(x) \cdot x + (1 - \mu(x))p_1\|}.$$

Also, h maps no point into its antipode and consequently is homotopic to the identity map of S^n. Since h is a closed map, the single valued function $\Phi h^{-1} : S^n \to S^n$ is continuous. Let $g = \Phi h^{-1}$ and we have $g^{-1}(q) = h\Phi^{-1}(q) = p_1$. Finally if $H : S^n \times I \to S^n$ is a homotopy from h to the identity map of S^n, then the composition map gH is a homotopy from g to Φ. Therefore $g \simeq \Phi \simeq f$ and this completes the proof.

THEOREM 42. For each map $f : S^n \to S^n$ ($n \geqslant 2$) there exists a map $g : S^{n-1} \to S^{n-1}$ such that f is homotopic to the suspension $S(g)$.

Proof: Only the case of an essential map f will be considered, the case of a nullhomotopic map being trivial. We will assume that the inverse image of p (the north pole) under f is the point p itself. In the light of Theorem 41 we see that this is not a restrictive assumption. It is possible to choose spherical neighborhoods U and V of p such that $f(U) \subset E^n_+$ and $V \subset f(U)$. Let $k : S^n \to S^n$ be a homeomorphism which maps $\overline{U}$ onto

E^n_+. Also there is a map $h : S^n \to S^n$ which pushes the boundary of V down onto the equator S^{n-1} and leaves each point in E^n_- fixed. Since neither h nor k^{-1} maps any point into its antipode, each is homotopic to the identity.

$$\begin{array}{ccc} S^n & \xrightarrow{\ f\ } & S^n \\ {\scriptstyle k}\downarrow & & \downarrow{\scriptstyle h} \\ S^n & \xdashrightarrow{\ g'\ } & S^n \end{array}$$

The map g' is defined as hfk^{-1} and is homotopic to the original map f; also, $g'(E^n_+) \subset E^n_+$ and $g'(E^n_-) \subset E^n_-$. Now set $g = (g' \mid S^{n-1}) : S^{n-1} \to S^{n-1}$ and we see that g' and $S(g)$ are homotopic since these two maps are never antipodal. This concludes the proof.

The symbol $[X, Y]$ is now introduced for topological spaces X and Y to represent the set of homotopy classes of maps from X to Y. The homotopy class of a map f is represented by $[f]$ and for $f : S^n \to S^n$, the degree of $[f]$ is defined as the degree of f. Our final result here will be that for each integer k there is exactly one homotopy class in $[S^n, S^n]$ with degree k. The proof will be by induction on n and the first step is to clear up the case $n = 1$.

THEOREM 43. For each integer k there is a homotopy class in $[S^1, S^1]$ of degree k.

The proof is left as an exercise.

THEOREM 44. Two maps $f, g : S^1 \to S^1$ having the same degree are homotopic.

Proof: As in the proof of Theorem 42, we may assume that $f(p) = g(p) = p$. There exist subdivisions K and K' of S^1 such that p is a vertex of K and simplicial approximations $\sigma, \tau : K' \to K$ of f and g. The idea now is to show that $|\sigma|$ and $|\tau|$ are homotopic.

Let $\{v_0, v_1, \ldots, v_a = v_0\}$ be the vertices of K listed in cyclic order and let K be oriented so that, for each j, $\langle v_j, v_{j+1} \rangle$ is an oriented simplex in K, and $v_0 = p$. Let $\{u_0, u_1, \ldots, u_b = u_0\}$ be the vertices of K' listed similarly and with $u_0 = v_0$. Also $\sigma(u_0) = \tau(u_0) = v_0$.

Next we wish to associate with each simplicial map $\alpha : K' \to K$ satisfying $\alpha(u_0) = v_0$ a sequence of integers $\{\varepsilon_0(\alpha), \varepsilon_1(\alpha), \ldots, \varepsilon_{b-1}(\alpha)\}$. Each $\varepsilon_i(\alpha)$ is defined by

$$\varepsilon_i(\alpha) = \begin{cases} +1 & \text{if } \alpha(u_i) = v_j, \ \alpha(u_{i+1}) = v_{j+1} \text{ for some } j, \\ 0 & \text{if } \alpha(u_i) = \alpha(u_{i+1}), \\ -1 & \text{if } \alpha(u_i) = v_j, \ \alpha(u_{i+1}) = v_{j-1} \text{ for some } j. \end{cases}$$

The simplicial map α is completely determined by the sequence $\{\varepsilon_i(\alpha)\}$. The plan now is to show that in the contiguity class of each such map α there is a map α_1 with $\alpha_1(u_0) = v_0$ and for which the sequence $\{\varepsilon_i(\alpha_1)\}$ has the following properties.

(1) There is an integer s such that for $i \leqslant s$, $\varepsilon_i(\alpha_1)$ are all $+1$ or are all -1.

(2) For $i > s$, $\varepsilon_i(\alpha_1) = 0$.

A map having the two properties of α_1 listed above will be called a *standard* map. To *reduce* α to a standard map will mean to replace α by a standard map in the same contiguity class. To show that such a reduction is possible, two operations on α will be considered.

First, suppose that $\varepsilon_p(\alpha)$ and $\varepsilon_q(\alpha)$ are consecutive nonzero elements of the sequence $\{\varepsilon_i(\alpha)\}$ and that their signs are different. For example, we may have that $\varepsilon_p(\alpha) = +1$, $\varepsilon_q(\alpha) = -1$, and $\varepsilon_i(\alpha) = 0$ for $p < i < q$. This means that for some j, $\alpha(u_p) = v_j$, $\alpha(u_i) = v_{j+1}$ for $p < i \leqslant q$ and $\alpha(u_{q+1}) = v_j$. Now a new map $\alpha' : K' \to K$ is given by

$$\alpha'(u_i) = v_j \qquad \text{for } p \leqslant i \leqslant q + 1$$
$$\alpha'(u_i) = \alpha(u_i) \qquad \text{otherwise.}$$

Then α is contiguous to α' and the sequence $\{\varepsilon_i(\alpha')\}$ differs from $\{\varepsilon_i(\alpha)\}$ only in that $\varepsilon_p(\alpha') = \varepsilon_q(\alpha') = 0$. Repetition of this process shows that in the contiguity class of α there is a map α'' such that all nonzero elements in the sequence $\{\varepsilon_i(\alpha'')\}$ have the same sign. A second process will be used to reduce the map α'' to a standard map. This time suppose that for some $p < q$, $\varepsilon_i(\alpha'') = 0$ for $p \leqslant i < q$ and that $\varepsilon_q(\alpha'') \neq 0$. The process for the case $\varepsilon_q(\alpha'') = +1$ will be illustrated. In this case, for some j, $\alpha''(u_i) = v_j$ for $p \leqslant i \leqslant q$ and $\alpha''(u_{q+1}) = v_{j+1}$. Define $\alpha_0 : K' \to K$ by

$$\alpha_0(u_i) = v_{j+1} \qquad \text{for } p < i \leqslant q$$
$$\alpha_0(u_i) = \alpha''(u_i) \qquad \text{otherwise.}$$

Now α'' and α_0 are contiguous and the sequence $\{\varepsilon_i(\alpha_0)\}$ differs from $\{\varepsilon_i(\alpha'')\}$ only in that $\varepsilon_q(\alpha_0) = 0$ and $\varepsilon_p(\alpha_0) = +1$. This means that a nonzero element in the sequence $\{\varepsilon_i(\alpha'')\}$ can be shifted to the left as far as the first nonzero element in that direction and the new sequence will represent a map in the contiguity class of α''. Repetition of this process completes the reduction of the original map α to a standard map α_1.

The next observation is that a standard map $\alpha_1 : K' \to K$ is completely determined by the integer $n = \deg(|\alpha_1|)$. This is true since the signs of the nonzero elements in the sequence $\{\varepsilon_i(\alpha_1)\}$ are all the sign of n and the number of such nonzero elements is $a|n|$ where a is the number of 1-simplexes in K.

To finish the proof, let us return to the original situation where $f = |\sigma|$ and $g = |\tau|$ and $\deg(f) = \deg(g)$. Then σ and τ may each be reduced to standard maps σ_1 and τ_1. Since σ and τ are in the contiguity classes of σ_1 and τ_1 respectively we have $|\sigma| \simeq |\sigma_1|$ and $|\tau| \simeq |\tau_1|$ (Theorem 13, Chapter II). Consequently, $\deg(|\sigma_1|) = \deg(|\sigma|) = \deg(f) = \deg(g) = \deg(|\tau|) = \deg(|\tau_1|)$ and we now have by the observation of the preceding paragraph that $\sigma_1 = \tau_1$. Finally, $f = |\sigma| \simeq |\sigma_1| = |\tau_1| \simeq |\tau| = g$ and this concludes the proof.

THEOREM 45. For $n > 0$, two maps $f, g : S^n \to S^n$ having the same degree are homotopic.

Proof: Theorem 44 is the case $n = 1$. Assume the theorem for $n = k$ and let $f, g : S^{k+1} \to S^{k+1}$. There exist maps $f', g' : S^k \to S^k$ such that $f \simeq S(f')$ and $g \simeq S(g')$ (Theorem 42). Now by Theorem 39, $\deg(f') = \deg(S(f')) = \deg(f) = \deg(g) = \deg(S(g')) = \deg(g')$ so that by the inductive hypothesis, f' and g' are homotopic. This implies (by Theorem 37) that $S(f')$ and $S(g')$ are homotopic. Finally, $f \simeq S(f') \simeq S(g') \simeq g$ and the proof is complete.

THEOREM 46. For each $n > 0$ there is a bijective function $\mu_n : [S^n, S^n] \to Z$ which assigns to each homotopy class its degree.

Proof: Consider the diagram

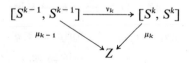

where $v_k([f]) = [S(f)]$. We already know from our previous results that v_k is bijective and that the diagram is commutative. Consequently, μ_k is bijective if and only if μ_{k-1} is bijective. However, we know from Theorems 43 and 44 that μ_1 is bijective and the result follows by induction.

EXERCISE 4

1. Define the suspension of a topological pair (X, A). Show that there is a covariant functor which assigns to each topological pair (X, A) the suspension $S(X, A)$ and to each map $f: (X, A) \to (Y, B)$ the suspended map $S(f)$.

2. Show that the functor of Problem 1 can be considered to be a functor on the homotopy category of topological pairs.

3. Show that the map $f: S^n \to S^n$ which changes the sign of the co-ordinate x^{n+1} has degree -1.

4. Consider S^1 to be the multiplicative group of complex numbers of absolute value one. Show that the function $f_n : S^1 \to S^1$ given by $f(z) = z^n$ has degree n.

5. Show that the following statement is equivalent to the Borsuk–Ulam Theorem: In each covering of S^n by $n+1$ closed sets there is a set containing a pair of antipodal points.

6. Show that every map $f: S^{2n} \to S^{2n}$ has a fixed point or sends some point into its antipode.

7. Show that there exists no map $f: S^{2n} \to S^{2n}$ such that x and $f(x)$ are orthogonal for all x.

8. Show that on an even-dimensional sphere there exists no nonzero continuous distribution of tangent vectors.

BIBLIOGRAPHY

Alexandroff, P., and H. Hopf. *Topologie.* Springer, 1935.

Bourgin, D. *Modern Algebraic Topology.* Macmillan, 1963.

Cairns, S. *Introductory Topology.* Ronald Press, 1961.

Eilenberg, S., and N. Steenrod. *Foundations of Algebraic Topology.* Princeton, 1952.

Hilton, P., and S. Wylie. *Homology Theory.* Cambridge, 1960.

Massey, W. *Algebraic Topology: An Introduction.* Harcourt, Brace & World, 1967.

Spanier, E. *Algebraic Topology.* McGraw-Hill, 1966.

Wallace, A. *Introduction to Algebraic Topology.* Pergamon, 1957.

INDEX OF SYMBOLS

INDEX